The Eat and Live Well Cookbook

Your Introduction to Healthy Living Guidebook

**Dr. Lewis Clark, D.C. BCIM, CCWP, CGP
Rhonda Clark, INHC**

Disclaimer

The book is for informational purposes only. Neither the publisher nor the author is engaged in rendering professional advice or services to the individual reader. The ideas, procedures and suggestions contained in this book are not intended as a substitute for consulting with your physician. All matters regarding your health require medical supervision. Neither the author nor the publisher shall be liable or responsible for any loss or damage allegedly arising from any information or suggestion in this book.

While the author has made every effort to provide accurate information at the time of publication, neither the publisher nor the author assumes any responsibility for errors or for changes that occur after publication. Further, the publisher does not have any control over and does not assume any responsibility for author or third-party websites or their content.

Dedication

This book is dedicated to our Lord and Savior Jesus Christ in thanksgiving for Him and what He has done for us.

I also want to thank my family and my practice members who allow me to have influence in their lives in the area of their health.

Contents

Why I Wrote This Book

"The preservation of health is easier than the cure of disease."
~B. J. Palmer

"Healthy citizens are the greatest asset any country can have."
~Winston Churchill

*"Do you not know that your bodies are temples of the Holy
Spirit, who is in you, whom you have received from God? You
are not your own; you were bought at a price. Therefore honor
God with your bodies."*
1 Corinthians 6:19-20 KJV

After more than 25 years of working with people to improve their health, I have found that optimal health is not common sense anymore. And the proof of this conclusion can be found in any public place in America, within your own family, or any other organization of the general population.

Every year in America, we have more obesity, more chronic illness, and more pain. Therefore, more drugs are prescribed and more surgeries are performed than in the previous year. However, our health as a nation continues to decline.

In an effort to reverse this trend and to provide the information and understanding necessary to obtain optimal health, my wife, Rhonda, and I have chosen to write this book.

It is my humble hope that those who read this book will have better health as a result of it. May it be a manual for your kitchen as you strive to improve the health of your family and loved ones!

How to Use This Book

This book is divided into two sections:

Section 1: Principles of Nutrition
Section 2: Healthful Recipes

I suggest you read section one first. It contains my best insights and advice about healthy and unhealthy diets. You will learn not only what to eat and what to avoid, but, more importantly, the reasons why you need to do so, backed by the latest research.

The second section includes recipes for breakfast, lunch, dinner, dessert, and breads. These recipes will help you to cook delicious, nutritious, creative, and surprisingly satisfying meals using items found in your pantry. These meals will improve your energy, digestion, weight, and moods without sacrificing flavor.

In the next chapter, you will learn why your diet is crucial for your good health and the quality of your life.

PRINCIPLES OF NUTRITION

Why is Diet So Important?

"You are what you get out of what you eat."
~Dr. Lewis M. Clark

"He who takes medicine and neglects to
diet wastes the skill of his doctors."
~Chinese Proverb

"Your diet is a bank account. Good food
choices are good investments."
~Bethenny Frankel

Why is diet so important?

The human cell, at its very base, requires two things: intelligence and fuel.

First of all, I personally believe that your body is fearfully and wonderfully made by God; so it is created intelligent. And I believe that this intelligence is what built your body from a single cell into more than 30 trillion cells working congruently and synergistically to not only survive but to thrive in life.[1]

I believe that the brain is the source that runs the body and gives the cells their orders on what to do and what not to do. Therefore, this communication channel, the nervous system, is called the master system. It controls the other systems and connects each cell of the body to the brain, which is the computer that runs the body.

Secondly, the human cell needs different kinds of fuel. For example, we need oxygen. Oxygen is critical for life and we can't sustain life without it. We also need stimulation from the electromagnetic field of the earth, we need sunlight, and, of course, we need food and water. Food is a vital fuel source for our cells. Our diet is one of the most important components of our health and quality of life.

Why is there so much confusion about diet?

Why are there so many different types of diets? Why is the internet loaded with information, which often seems confusing and contradictory? Well, that's a good question!

Over the next few chapters, I hope to explain why I recommend the diet that I do, and to give you historic as well as scientific evidence to prove the principles that we will lay out for you in this book.

Optimal health doesn't happen naturally. It has to be planned. The standard American diet is aptly called SAD because it's sad, very sad! Some researchers state that the majority of Americans are undernourished. That doesn't mean they are underweight. No, they're overweight but undernourished, meaning their diet has too many calories but too few nutrients for their cells to maintain optimal health.

---

[1]   https://pubmed.ncbi.nlm.nih.gov/23829164/

Therefore, chronic illness is rampant, as is, obesity, chronic fatigue, and other disorders related to low-functioning or chronically sick cells.

What can we do about it?

Well, we must first look back to a time when Americans were much healthier than they are today. We can also look around the world at other civilizations and start to get a picture of what is necessary to get ourselves back to optimal health.

Finally, we will find that a review of the current authentic research on diet and nutrition will direct us to the diet that we were created to eat. This is the diet that I'm going to cover in the next few chapters.

In the next chapter, you will learn the difference between real foods and unhealthy foods. You will, also, learn what the biggest problems with food are and how you can overcome them.

Why Real Foods Matter?

One who eats plain food is healthy.
~Japanese Proverb

"I don't eat junk foods and I don't think junk thoughts."
~Peace Pilgrim

"In general, the more food we eat in its natural state – without additives – and the less it is refined, the healthier it will be for us."
~Ezra Taft Benson

Why does real food matter?

Real food matters because your body is created intelligently. Our Creator gave us everything we need to be healthy, and a system to protect us from poisons and toxins. This system is called your immune system. Your body is genetically engineered to detect what is food and what is toxic.

The problem today, especially in industrialized countries like America, are food products. Though they are made from food, food products are food made by man, and not food made by God. These food products are not found in nature. They have been modified in some way, and therefore, they seem suspicious to your immune system.

My patients often ask me, "Why are there so many problems with food today?"

Well, that's a complex and multi-faceted problem. However, one of the reasons is that there have been changes in agriculture causing our food source to change, and, therefore, it seems foreign and can cause an immune response.

For example, food by God doesn't have labels. However, most of the food in our grocery store has labels that tell us what's in the food. Not only have we never heard of most of these ingredients, but we can't even pronounce many of them!

And certainly, our grandmother would not recognize them as food because they aren't food, they're food products. Much of the food that we put into our bodies is loaded with preservatives, additives, toxins, and other harmful chemicals.

So we must get back to eating real food. And that includes a diet that has its foundation in vegetables, fruits, and healthy meats.

People always ask me, "What do you mean by healthy meats?"

I mean meats that come from a healthy animal; an animal that is eating its God-intended diet. Not one that has been cooped up and fed different food than what it would normally eat in the wild. In particular, I mean grain-fed and feedlot beef cattle. Obviously, one of the major problems that we have in America is the way we have chosen to do our farming and raising our livestock. Their living conditions are as important as what they are fed.

If I ask my patients, "What do cows eat?" they always say the same thing. They say grass. However, what did the cow eat that supplied the ground meat or steak that you find in your grocery store? Well, unless it says grass-fed, it was fed grains. So it was fed corn, and other grains to increase its weight. This diet helps to accelerate their growth and make them unnaturally obese, which increases a company's profitability.

If you change an animal's diet, you also change the nutritive value of its meat. So we get healthy meats from animals that eat their normal diet for at least a majority of their life. For cows, it's grass-fed beef. For chicken, it is free-range chicken. For pigs, it is pasture-raised pork.

For this reason, our family started a grass-fed beef farm. We raise, sell, and eat 100% grass fed beef. When you change an animal's diet, from grass to grain, you change the type of fat in the meat from anti inflammatory omega 3s to pro inflammatory omega 6s. This is one of the great tragedies of our food supply.

These things are important for your overall health. Often these animals are also given harmful drugs like antibiotics and hormones. Obviously, if such drugs are given to those animals, they will also end up in us.

What about vegetables?

Well, vegetables should be your primary source of most nutrients as well as fiber. Fiber is critical for the health of the microbes that live inside your digestive tract. The more vegetables you take in, the more diverse is your fiber intake, and the more diverse bacteria in your intestines.

Many studies have been done in the last decade on the microbiome, which is the collection of microbes in the human gut. It has been called the decade of the microbiome because these microbes influence all aspects of our health including our immune system, brain health, and even the expression of our genes. They affect depression, cancer, longevity, and metabolic and inflammatory disorders.[2]

So it's essential to feed these microbes and maintain a healthy environment for them. Anything that kills these microbes affects our health. The most damage to our gut, immune system, and overall microbe health is caused by antibiotics. Unfortunately, antibiotics are now used without discretion in our culture and we're paying the price with poor health.

Many times when working with a patient, and digging down to find the start of their health decline, I find the decline started after use of antibiotics. Research confirms recovery time is 6 months to 2 years for the gut and microbiome after one round of antibiotics. You can easily see the problem.

In addition, pesticides and herbicides are commonly used on vegetables and fruits during commercial farming. These chemicals have an adverse impact on our health. More than 50,000 chemicals have been introduced into our environment since the Second World War.[3]

These include older chemicals like DDT and PCBs, pollutants like mercury, lead, and dioxins; newer pesticides and plastic ingredients; and newer compounds such as bisphenol A, an ingredient in plastics and flame-retarding compounds called polybrominated diphenyl ethers.[4]

These chemicals affect our detoxification and elimination systems, particularly the liver, and even more specifically, our glutathione levels. Glutathione is our body's number one antioxidant. Its levels are

---

[2]   https://www.sciencedirect.com/science/article/pii/S1021949819300122
[3]   https://www.epa.gov/tsca-inventory
[4]   https://www.nationalgeographic.com/science/health-and-human-body/human-body/chemicals-within-us/

depleted by this heavy load of environmental and food-borne toxins. Once they are depleted, other parts of our immune system become upregulated, leading to food sensitivities, leaky gut, autoimmune disorders, and cancers.

What about fruits?

Fruits contain an abundance of fiber and nutrients. However, fruits also contain fructose. That's why they are sweet. There's nothing wrong with fructose in small amounts. However, some people have become fruit junkies. So they are consuming way too much sugar.

I have a simple rule: Two to one: Two vegetables for every fruit. Among the fruits, the berries are the most beneficial to your health because they have the least amount of sugar and the most amount of fiber.

Other real foods that should be included in your diet include nuts and seeds as well as herbs and spices. They add quality to our health and satisfaction to our food.

Finally, what about fats?

Fat has gotten a bad reputation in America because of the false premise that a low-fat diet prevents heart disease. Unfortunately, since this concept was introduced in the 1970s, heart disease has skyrocketed. Now most researchers and health professionals are realizing that not only is fat NOT the cause of heart disease, but healthy fats are absolutely essential for good health.

Fat is vital for the optimal functioning of the brain, nervous system, and hormone health. Your brain is made up mostly of fat. And omega-3 fats are especially good for brain health because a type of omega-3 fat called DHA (docosahexaenoic acid) is abundant in the neurons and axons in our brain.[5]

So the questions should not be, "Should I have fat?" You must have fat. Instead, the question should be, "What type of fat should I be consuming?" Again, we must return to the premise of **real food matters** and **food by God, not food by man**. So, the more natural the fat, the better.

Man-made trans fats like partially hydrogenated fat, as well as fats like canola that have been changed or heavily refined won't provide the nutrients that you need for optimal health. On the contrary, these fats can harm your overall health; they can be a source of free radicals; and they can increase oxidized stress.

One of the problems with oils is that they can become rancid if they are manufactured improperly or used improperly in the cooking process. As a rule, saturated fats can tolerate high temperatures, whereas unsaturated fats cannot.

How can we know whether it is saturated or unsaturated fat?

Well, if it is a solid at room temperature, it is saturated fat. Saturated fat has more bonds to hold it together, and therefore it can tolerate more heat. So, fats like coconut oil or any high-temperature cooking oil are saturated and an excellent source of fat.

Oils like avocado oil, even though liquid, can handle higher temperatures. Oils like olive oil may be used to lightly sauté or at room temperature in dressings, and such.

---

5   https://www.ncbi.nlm.nih.gov/pmc/articles/PMC4404917/

However, always remember the rule: make sure that the oil is coming from a good source, a healthy source. Then find out what temperature it can sustain.

To summarize, the basis of the best diet for optimal health is vegetables and fruits in a 2:1 ratio, healthy meats (that is, meats from healthy animals), nuts, seeds, herbs, spices, and healthy fats.

In the next chapter, we will learn about one of the biggest dangers to our health: chronic inflammation. We will learn the importance of avoiding inflammatory foods and having foods that prevent and fight inflammation.

3

Why an Anti-Inflammatory Diet?

"Eat food. Not too much. Mostly plants."
~Michael Pollan

"A healthy outside starts from the inside."
~Robert Urich

"The doctor of the future will no longer treat the human frame
with drugs, but rather will cure and prevent disease with nutrition."
~Thomas Edison

I am often asked about chronic inflammation by my patients.

Inflammation is a critical component of healing. However, when it becomes chronic, it is profoundly detrimental to our health. Chronic inflammation is a state in which white blood cells attack healthy tissues and organs, resulting in a chronic inflammatory process that persists for months or years. According to a Harvard Medical School report, inflammation plays a central role in many non-infectious diseases like rheumatoid arthritis, cancer, heart disease, diabetes, asthma, and Alzheimer's. Once this low-level inflammation begins, it can persist even when there is no apparent injury or disease.[6]

So how do we get inflammation?

Some of the common causes of chronic inflammation are:

- a pro-inflammatory diet
- food allergies
- imbalanced gut bacteria
- being overweight and obese
- stress
- smoking
- a sedentary lifestyle
- environmental pollution
- toxic chemicals in our cleaning and beauty products

Foods that can cause inflammation include sugars (especially fructose), refined carbohydrates including white flour products, gluten, casein, unhealthy fats like trans fats (especially in partially hydrogenated vegetable oils), MSG (monosodium glutamate), artificial sweeteners like aspartame, and alcohol.[7]

Doc, how do we get out of this inflammation if we already have it?

An anti-inflammatory diet and a healthy lifestyle are your best weapons to fight chronic inflammation.

---

[6] https://www.health.harvard.edu/staying-healthy/understanding-inflammation
[7] https://draxe.com/health/inflammation-at-the-root-of-most-diseases/

An anti-inflammatory diet includes:

- A variety of colorful vegetables and fruits (Eat your colors.)
- Fiber-rich whole grains
- Skinless free-range poultry prepared in healthy ways without added saturated and trans fat
- A variety of wild-caught fish such as salmon, trout, and herring that are rich in omega-3 fatty acids
- Nuts, seeds, legumes, herbs, and spices
- Healthy oils like extra-virgin olive oil, flaxseed oil, avocado oil, sesame oil, and coconut oil
- Minimal high-calorie and low-nutrient foods. Avoid foods containing simple sugars and refined carbs, sodas, processed meat, and foods containing partially hydrogenated vegetable oils. Hydrogenated oils are found in candy, margarine, processed foods, and even in your favorite coffee creamers.

In addition,

- Decide on the optimum amount to eat each day depending on your age, gender, and physical activity
- Keep an eye on your portion sizes when you eat out.
- Read Nutrition Facts labels carefully to know the amount of healthy and unhealthy nutrients in a food or beverage, especially added sugars.
- If you drink alcohol, drink in moderation.

An anti-inflammatory diet need not be bland or boring. You can choose a healthy diet based on your personal food preferences. The recipes given in this book will help you to prepare and eat foods that are healthy and delicious.

A healthy lifestyle means work-life balance, regular exercise, stress management, healthy recreational activities, and quality time with family and friends. (See the appendix for the ninety-day probation plan.)

Exercise and physical activity: Aim for about 75 minutes of vigorous exercise or 150 minutes of moderate exercise each week. In addition to regular exercise sessions, increase your daily physical activity. For example, walk short distances instead of riding, take the stairs instead of the elevator, park farther away, and play sports. Try to spread your activity throughout the day and week. Try to avoid prolonged periods of inactivity. If you are a knowledge worker, move about for a few moments every 45-60 minutes.

Stop Tobacco: Don't smoke, vape, or use tobacco or nicotine products — and avoid secondhand smoke or vapor.[8]

The food we eat can either be inflammatory or anti-inflammatory. When we choose to eat anti-inflammatory foods, we are choosing health and wellbeing over disease and debility.

In the next chapter, you will learn about gluten and how it threatens your health and life. You will learn why we recommend that you avoid or minimize gluten in your diet.

---

[8] https://www.heart.org/en/healthy-living/healthy-eating/eat-smart/ nutrition-basics/aha-diet-and-lifestyle-recommendations

4

Why Gluten-Free?

"We may all be sensitive to gluten from a neurological standpoint."
~Dr. David Perlmutter

*"It is a strange feeling to realize that what you regularly eat
has been making you really sick."*
~Steven Magee

*"Small changes in wheat protein structure can spell the
difference between a devastating immune response to wheat
protein versus no immune response at all."*
~Dr. William Davis

What is gluten?

Gluten is the main protein of wheat grains and consists mainly of
gliadin and glutenin. Similar proteins exist in barley, oats, and rye,
and are collectively called gluten. Gluten is also found in other grains
such as triticale, malt, spelt, and Kamut.

Composition of Wheat[9]

Wheat kernel					
Protein (8-15%)		Starch (60-70%)	Moisture (10-15%)	Lipid (1-2%)	Ash (4%)
Albumin/ Globulin (10-15%)	Gluten (85-90%)				
	Gliadin (50%)				
	Glutenin (50%)				

The average daily gluten intake in a Western diet is thought to be 5–20 g/day and it has been implicated in several disorders.[10]

Unfortunately, gluten is found not only in these grains but in most processed foods. It improves flavor, texture, and moisture retention in processed foods. Therefore, gluten is added to candies, confectionery, butter, ice cream, medications, seafood, processed meat, vegetarian meat substitutes, seasonings, stuffings, marinades, dressings, industrial bakery products, and low-protein flours.[11]

Why should we worry about gluten, Doc?

Gluten is responsible for diseases such as

1. Celiac disease: It is an immune-mediated disease that affects about 1% of Western populations. Toxic peptides within the gliadin

---

9   Biesiekierski JR. Review Article. What is gluten? *Journal of Gastroenterology and Hepatology* 2017; 32 (Suppl. 1): 78–81 https://onlinelibrary.wiley.com/doi/pdf/10.1111/jgh.13703

10 Biesiekierski JR. Review Article. What is gluten? *Journal of Gastroenterology and Hepatology* 2017; 32 (Suppl. 1): 78–81 https://onlinelibrary.wiley.com/doi/pdf/10.1111/jgh.13703

11 Kucek LK, Veenstra LD, Amnuaycheewa Pet al. A grounded guide to gluten: how modern genotypes and processing impact wheat sensitivity. Compr. Rev. Food Sci. Food Saf.2015;14: 285–302.

fraction of the gluten protein trigger an immune response leading to inflammation and leaky gut. The only known treatment is a lifelong, strict gluten-free diet.

2. Wheat allergy: Wheat allergy is an allergic reaction caused by eating foods containing wheat gluten or by inhaling wheat flour. It occurs when the body produces antibodies to wheat gluten. The symptoms usually develop within minutes to hours after ingestion and may include skin rash, itching, swelling, chest pain, breathing difficulty, and even life-threatening anaphylaxis.[12]

3. Non-celiac gluten sensitivity: Non-celiac gluten sensitivity (NCGS) is a condition where gluten ingestion triggers intestinal and extraintestinal symptoms such as bloating, abdominal pain, diarrhea, wind, altered bowel habits, fatigue, headache, joint or muscle pain, skin rash, anemia, depression, and anxiety.[13] However, unlike celiac disease, gluten intolerance doesn't usually cause long-term harm to the body.

No wonder, neurologist and author, Dr. David Perlmutter says "Gluten is this generation's tobacco."

"But, Doc, I thought you were a Bible believer, and the Bible says that wheat is good."

That's true but the problem in America, and other industrial countries, comes from what we have done to our foods. Wheat has changed dramatically from the wheat that was available generations earlier. I've said it before and I'll say again that if I could eat the foods that the Lord Jesus ate, I would eat it.

---

[12] https://www.mayoclinic.org/diseases-conditions/wheat-allergy/symptoms-causes/syc-20378897
[13] Biesiekierski JR, Iven J. Non-coeliac gluten sensitivity: piecing the puzzle together. *United European Gastroenterol J* 2015; 3: 160–5.

Dr. William Davis in his book, *Wheat Belly*, states that ancient wheat had 14 chromosomes versus modern wheat, which has 42 chromosomes.[14] So this wheat looks different to your immune system. Also, we treat modern wheat with an enzyme called transglutaminase. This process of deamidation and/or transamidation can cross-link wheat proteins together, which our immune system may not recognize.[15]

The transglutaminase enzyme also increases the stability of protein against proteinases and affects the elimination of foreign protein. It can also lead to leaky gut syndrome and celiac disease.[16]

I'm not saying that all grains are bad, they're not. Whole grains and sprouted grains have nutritional value. However, the most common food sensitivity is to wheat.

Therefore, concerning wheat, there are two types of people.

- Firstly, everyone **should** be off wheat because it is inflammatory and affects our blood sugar more than even simple sugar.
- Secondly, those who have an immune reaction to the gliadin protein found in wheat **must** be on a permanent gluten-free diet.

Why should gluten be avoided?

1. Gluten causes gut inflammation in at least 80% of the population.
2. Since gliadin, the main problem-causing gluten protein, is similar in structure to other proteins found in tissues of organs such as the thyroid or the pancreas, antibodies against gliadin can end up attacking those organs and ultimately

---

[14] https://www.ncbi.nlm.nih.gov/pmc/articles/PMC4488568/
[15] https://pubmed.ncbi.nlm.nih.gov/16528904/
[16] https://www.ncbi.nlm.nih.gov/pmc/articles/PMC4502714/

cause autoimmune diseases like hypothyroidism and type 1 diabetes.

3. Antibodies against gluten have also been shown to attack heart tissue and cause heart diseases.
4. Gluten damages intestinal cells and causes a leaky gut, which can result in autoimmune attacks on the body.

So what's the solution?

Gluten-related disorders are increasing in the US and may affect more than one in ten Americans.[17] Those who are sensitive to gluten must follow a permanent gluten-free diet.

However, even for those who may not be sensitive to gluten, avoiding or minimizing gluten in their diet has many health benefits such as fat loss, decreased inflammation, improved digestion, and increased energy levels.

In his book, *Wheat Belly*, Dr. William Davis recommends eliminating all foods containing wheat, barley, rye, spelt, and certain oats. He also advises us to cut out sugar, salt, high-fructose corn syrup, sugary foods, rice, soda, fruit juice, trans fats, fried foods, and cured meats.

Those on a gluten-free diet have to check food labels to make sure they don't contain hidden gluten. The FDA defines gluten-free as the allowable level of gluten detectable to 20 parts per million (ppm), or less.

What is a gluten-free diet?

The gluten-free diet includes vegetables, fruit (especially berries, apples, and oranges), grass-fed, free-range meat and eggs, raw nuts, raw seeds, legumes, beans, herbs, spices, and plant-based

---

[17] https://www.ncbi.nlm.nih.gov/pmc/articles/PMC3908912/

oils such as olive, avocado, and coconut. You may also eat limited quantities of fruit such as pineapple, papaya, mango, and banana, and whole grains such as quinoa, millet, and amaranth.

In the next chapter, you will learn the surprising reasons why dairy is dangerous to your health and what to do about it.

5

Why Dairy-Free?

*"Never cry over spilled milk, because
it may have been poisoned."*
~W C Fields

*"Any food that requires enhancing by the use of chemical
substances should in no way be considered a food.*
~John H. Tobe

*"Our deeply-rooted beliefs about the wholesomeness
of milk and dairy products should be reconsidered
under careful, scientific evaluation."*
~Bodo Melnik

So, what's wrong with dairy?

The first problem with dairy has to do with processing. The FDA bans the interstate sale or distribution of raw milk, though states may adopt their own laws on raw milk sales. All milk sold across state lines must be pasteurized and meet the standards of the US Pasteurized Milk Ordinance.[18]

---

[18]   https://milk.procon.org/raw-milk-law1s-state-by-state/

Therefore, almost all dairy is pasteurized and homogenized. This means that milk is spun at a high rate of speed and heated, which destroys much of its nutrition value and, changes milk, to the point, where it becomes suspicious to our immune system.

More importantly, many dairy cows are given hormones, in order, to increase their milk production. Most of them are fed grains to change their fat. Many of these animals are also given antibiotics and other drugs because of the close quarters in which they live.

Finally, the molecular form of dairy is very similar to gluten. Therefore, you can have a cross-reaction where your immune system also reacts to dairy. If you are gluten-free or know you need to be gluten-free, you must also consider your body's reaction to dairy. Even after following a gluten-free diet, people with celiac disease may continue to suffer from inflammation and gastrointestinal symptoms. This is usually because of sensitivity to cow's milk protein, especially casein.[19]

Dairy and gluten are the two most inflammatory foods, as well as the most immune-reactive foods. Therefore, it's my recommendation to review ingesting problem foods including what's typical of these two proteins. This means following an **elimination/provocation diet** for a minimum of 4-6 weeks. You remove gluten and dairy from your diet completely. Then, after a period no less than four weeks, preferably six, you add one of those foods back and see how your body responds.

If you feel any new symptoms, especially headaches, joint pain, fatigue or brain fog, you are likely to have a food sensitivity.

You can choose to go gluten-free or dairy-free but without knowing the exact cause of your symptoms; you may not get the right solution.

---

[19]   https://www.ncbi.nlm.nih.gov/pmc/articles/PMC1810502/

A professionally administered Elimination/Provocation diet as well as more thorough testing between both raw and cooked foods gives the most accurate result.

The best way to get to the root of the problem is to schedule a consultation with a licensed, professional nutritional coach that will work with you towards your wellness goals.

In the next chapter, you will learn why "sugar is the new smoking," that is, it's considered to be as harmful to your health as smoking.

6

Why Sugar-Free?

*"What is sweet in the mouth is not
always good in the stomach."*
~Danish Proverb

*"If God hadn't meant for us to eat sugar,
he wouldn't have invented dentists."*
~Ralph Nader

*"Sugar fans the flames of inflammation in your body, as it is
a dirty fuel that was never intended to be our primary fuel."*
~Dr. Joseph Mercola

Why is sugar harmful to our health?

Sugar is not an immune-stimulus food like gluten and dairy. However, sugar has its own dangers. Sugar raises our blood glucose levels and provides empty calories. Over time, excess sugar leads to insulin resistance and excess fat deposition in the body. It also robs our body of nutrients that are needed to digest sugar.

Would you reward your children and grandchildren with a treat that you knew would decrease their health? It may seem to you, as if, you are depriving your loved ones of sugar, but you are actually depriving them of sickness, drugs, hospital visits, and diminished quality of life. In fact, I think that we have, unfortunately, lost sight of what our older, mature senior years should look and feel like.

Ironically, the reason for overweight and obesity is more likely to be either a food sensitivity or too much sugar in our diet instead of dietary fat.

So, you want to know "How much sugar is too much?"

Though the FDA by no means should be considered a health authority, even they say that you should not consume more than 30 grams of added sugar per day. However, the average American consumes almost 66 pounds of added sugar in one year. So, we consume about 25 teaspoons (100 grams) of added sugar daily; three times more than the FDA recommends as healthy.

You may be thinking, "I would never consume that much sugar." Well, you might be surprised. Why don't you actually count all the grams of sugar you consume over the next 1-2 days?

Let's take a few foods or a few products commonly found in our diet, like a soda, for example. A serving of soda will probably have 40 or more grams of sugar. That is half of the average American's sugar intake and already 10 grams more than the FDA recommends.

So how much is 40 grams of sugar?

I'm glad you asked. One teaspoon of sugar equals four grams. Most brands of soda contain 10 teaspoons of sugar (that is, 40 grams). Wow! No wonder we're fatigued, overweight, and in poor health.

Put it to the test and check your diet. Count the grams of sugar that you consume every day and then calculate how many pounds of sugar you consume in a year. It's going to be frighteningly close to 100 pounds of sugar.

So, Doc, are you saying that we can't have any sugar at all?

Absolutely not! God created us with a desire for sugar. Even breast milk has a sweetness to it. What I'm saying is that we must find natural sources for our sugar, including what we've already talked about, in fruit.

However, did you know that taste is an acquired sense? This means that your taste—the way your brain interprets the type of food that you're ingesting—can change within just a few weeks. Therefore, you can also change your sugar cravings in a few weeks based on what you give your body.

Unfortunately, because of artificial sweeteners and the massive amount of super-sweet products that we consume, our taste buds are so dulled that they don't even sense most fruit as being sweet or satisfying. Excessive artificial sweeteners may make us crave sugar more because we don't get the gratification from real sugar.

Now, a word of warning. Most of us will need at least four weeks of a sugar fast to reset the sensitivity of our taste buds.[20] However, the sugar fast will open your eyes to the effects of sugar on your overall health and physique.

For example, I had a patient who cut sugar out of his diet. He wasn't obese and he didn't think he consumed a lot of sugar. However, he dropped 26 pounds and was back to the weight of his early 20s.

---

[20]   https://pubmed.ncbi.nlm.nih.gov/26607941/

Too much added sugar doesn't just make us fat. It can also make us sick. Also, high-sugar products dull our taste buds and cause a snowball effect. A sugar-restricted diet helps to reset not only your taste buds but also your waistline, your energy, and your overall health.

In the pages to come, we've included recipes to help you make the transition in your kitchen for your family toward real food. And that doesn't mean that you sacrifice taste or satisfaction because I believe that food is a blessing from God. God could have created our food bland, flat, and insipid, but he didn't. Food is emotional! Food is to be enjoyed, and it is to be shared with family and friends. Most importantly, the food that we enjoy should be the food that helps us to maintain and achieve optimal health.

In the recipes to come, you're going to find that fruits and vegetables are free of gluten and dairy. You'll also find that in most, if not all, of these recipes, we will be using only natural sweeteners such as honey, maple syrup, and dried fruits. They will allow you to satisfy your desire for sweets without causing you to develop insulin resistance. More importantly, they will boost your energy and, ultimately, change your taste buds.

So, with that said, I bid you welcome to your journey to optimal health. May God bless your efforts!

HEALTHFUL RECIPES

Recipes

"I have the simplest tastes. I am always satisfied with the best."
~Oscar Wilde

"A recipe has no soul. You, as the cook,
must bring soul to the recipe"
~Thomas Keller

"At home I serve the kind of food I know the story behind"
~Michael Pollan

The recipes in the following pages will help you to:

1. learn how to make delicious, healthful real-food, home-cooked meals for your family quickly and easily
2. learn how to cook low-carb meals without spending tons of time in the kitchen
3. save money on food without sacrificing your health or taste buds
4. create meals that promote health, happiness, and healing
5. recalibrate the kitchen experience and eliminate meal planning stress
6. learn a range of delightful options for weeknight dinners
7. prepare meals in just a few hours and enjoy weeks of easy, no-fuss dinners

8. make a practical meal plan to meet your healthy eating goals
9. enjoy healthy whole-food meals, regardless of the type of diet you prefer to follow
10. learn to go sugar-free, gluten-free, and dairy-free
11. learn how to eat more healthy fats
12. make deliciously simple nutrient-dense allergy-friendly meals
13. make easy delicious gluten-free meals on a budget
14. learn to make freshly baked gluten-free bread, hot from the oven
15. make delicious gluten-free breakfasts with dairy-free options
16. cook meals that nourish your body and support the body's natural detoxification process
17. nourish your family with a whole-food, nutrient-dense diet
18. make you leaner, stronger, and healthier
19. help you to balance your macros (macronutrients: protein, carbohydrates and, fats)
20. fit your goals and your budget

2

Breakfast Recipes

*Vegetables shouldn't just be for dinner; think about
vegetables for any time of day, including breakfast."*
~Dr. William Davis

*"Processed foods not only extend the shelf life,
but they extend the waistline as well."*
~Karen Sessions

*"Those who think they have no time for healthy eating
will sooner or later have to find time for illness."*
~Edward Stanley

EASY EGG MUFFINS

INGREDIENTS:

12 eggs

½ package of uncured cooked pork or turkey bacon (chopped)

3 tablespoons cooked chopped onions

1 cup cooked chopped spinach (remove excess water)

Salt and pepper, to taste

1-1½ cups sheep cheese

½ cup tomatoes, diced

DIRECTIONS:

1. Preheat the oven to 375 degrees. Line muffin pan with paper liners and spray with coconut oil.
2. In a large bowl whisk the eggs, salt, and pepper until smooth.
3. Add the bacon, onion, spinach, cheese, and tomatoes to the egg mixture and stir until combined.
4. Divide the egg mixture evenly among the muffin cups.
5. Bake for 15-19 minutes or until eggs are set.

GLUTEN FREE QUICHE

INGREDIENTS:

1 (9 inch) gluten free unbaked or frozen pie crust

6 large eggs

¾ cup unsweetened almond milk

1 tsp salt

¼ tsp black pepper

¼ cup green onions, chopped

1 cup cooked ham, chopped

1 ½ cups goat cheese, grated

2 tbsp fresh basil, chopped

1 tsp dried parsley

INSTRUCTIONS:

1. Preheat oven to 375 degrees.
2. In a large bowl, whisk together eggs, milk, parsley, salt and pepper.
3. In a separate bowl add remaining ingredients and combine well and sprinkle into the pie crust.
4. Pour the egg mixture over the top. Sprinkle remaining cheese on top of the egg mixture.
5. Bake for 45-55 minutes until the center is set.

GRAINLESS PANCAKES

INGREDIENTS:

2 small ripe bananas, mashed

¼ cup cashew or almond butter

2 eggs

½ teaspoon baking soda

1 teaspoon vanilla

½ teaspoon cinnamon

DIRECTIONS:

1. Mash bananas until smooth, no lumps.
2. Add all of the ingredients to a bowl.
3. Mix well. Grease a griddle or pan and turn on medium heat.
4. Keep pancakes small, that will make it easier to flip.
5. Cook until brown on both sides.
6. Grainless pancakes take a bit longer to cook and can have a burnt look to them because of the sugar in the bananas.

BREAKFAST CASSEROLE

INGREDIENTS:

1 pound sausage, cooked and drained

1 cup chopped onions

2 medium potatoes, peeled and cubed

2 cups shredded goat cheese

¼ cup Gluten free flour

1 cup almond milk

2 tsp salt

2 tbsp chopped fresh basil or ½ teaspoon dried basil

½ teaspoon pepper

12 eggs

2 cups spinach

DIRECTIONS:

1. Pre heat oven to 350 degrees. Grease a rectangular baking dish, 13x9x2 inches works well.

2. Layer sausage, onions, potatoes, spinach, and cheese in the dish.

3. Stir remaining ingredients in a bowl until blended. Pour this mixture over layers.

4. Bake uncovered 30 to 35 minutes or until golden brown and set.

CROCKPOT COOKING: LIGHTLY GREASE CROCKPOT AND COOK ON LOW FOR 8 HOURS.

EGG SURPRISE

INGREDIENTS:

1 piece gluten-free bread

1 egg

Dairy free butter

Spray oil

DIRECTIONS:

1. Spray pan with oil.
2. Cut a hole out of the center of the bread (or use a cookie cutter) then butter both sides of the bread.
3. Place the bread in pan on medium/high heat.
4. Crack an egg and place it in the hole that was cut out.
5. Cook until the egg is cooked on both sides.

POWER SMOOTHIE

INGREDIENTS:

½ cup unsweetened vanilla almond milk (more or less depending on your taste)

½ frozen banana

¼ ripe avocado

1 teaspoon ground flaxseed

1 tablespoon collagen

1 large handful of spinach

½ teaspoon cinnamon

½ can full fat coconut milk

½ cup berries of choice

INSTRUCTIONS:

1. Add all ingredients to blender.
2. Blend and enjoy!

MONKEY SMOOTHIE

INGREDIENTS:

½ can of full fat coconut milk

1 cup of almond milk (More or less depending on your desired consistency)

¼ cup cashew butter

1 scoop of protein powder

½ banana

½ teaspoon of cinnamon

½ teaspoon vanilla

1 tbsp MCT or coconut oil

DIRECTIONS:

1. Add all ingredients to blender
2. Blend and enjoy!

GLUTEN FREE PANCAKES

INGREDIENTS:

2 cups gluten free all-purpose flour

½ teaspoon xanthan gum

2 teaspoons baking powder

1 teaspoon salt

½ tsp baking soda

2 large eggs

1 ½ cups dairy free milk (regular or unsweetened almond milk)

¼ cup coconut oil, melted

1/3 cup pure maple syrup

1 teaspoon vanilla extract

2 teaspoon fresh lemon juice

DIRECTIONS:

1. In a medium bowl, whisk together the gluten free flour, xanthan gum, baking powder, salt, and baking soda. Set aside.
2. In a large bowl, whisk together the eggs, milk, oil, maple syrup, vanilla extract, and lemon.
3. Add the dry ingredients to the wet ingredients and stir until completely combined. NOTE: Pancake batter will be thick and will puff up as it sits.
4. Heat a griddle on low heat. When the griddle is hot, spray with cooking oil, then scoop the batter onto the griddle, about ¼ cup at a time.
5. Cook on the first side and then flip when little bubbles start to appear. Cook until the other side is browned and cooked through.

_____

_____

_____

_____

_____

_____

_____

_____

_____

_____

_____

_____

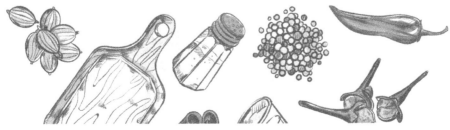

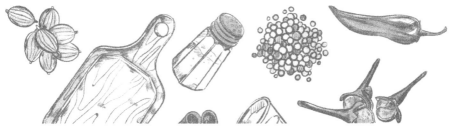

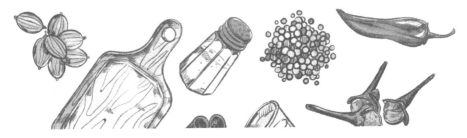

_____

_____

_____

_____

_____

_____

_____

_____

_____

_____

_____

_____

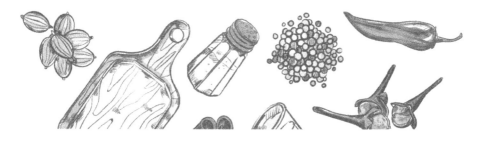

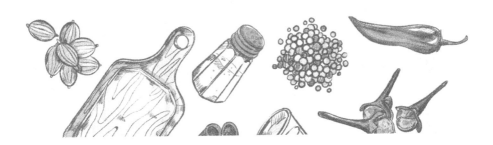

3

Lunch Recipes

"Don't dig your grave with your own knife and fork."
~English Proverb

"To eat is a necessity, but to eat intelligently is an art."
~La Rochefoucauld

"Today more than 95% of all chronic disease is caused by food choice, toxic food ingredients, nutritional deficiencies, and lack of physical exercise."
~Mike Adams

KALE SALAD

INGREDIENTS:

1 bunch kale

Salt and pepper to taste

Balsamic dressing enough to coat kale well

¼ cup sliced almonds

¼ cup dried cranberries

DIRECTIONS:

1. Remove stems and chop kale into bite sized pieces.
2. Combine kale and balsamic dressing in large bowl.
3. Stir well.
4. Season with salt and pepper. Stir in almonds and cranberries.

TIP: best to soak the kale and dressing over night or for a few hours in the refrigerator to soften kale. Then add almonds and cranberries when ready to serve.

BROCCOLI SALAD

INGREDIENTS:

1 bunch broccoli, cut into bite size pieces

1/3 cup red onion, chopped

½ cup dried cranberries

2 tbsp fresh cilantro, chopped

Salt and pepper, to taste

¼ cup sliced almonds or pumpkin seeds

½ cup uncured salami

½-1 cup of mayonnaise

3 tbsp apple cider vinegar

2 tbsp honey

INSTRUCTIONS:

1. In a large bowl, combine all ingredients and stir well.
2. Chill in the refrigerate for two hours before serving.

BROCCOLI SLAW SALAD WITH DRESSING

Salad:

INGREDIENTS:

5 cups broccoli florets

½ cup raisins

1/3 cup slivered almonds

1 carrot, peeled and shredded

1 cup cabbage, roughly chopped (red or green)

½ cup yellow onion, finely chopped

1 tbsp. fresh cilantro, chopped fine

Dressing:

INGREDIENTS:

½ cup mayonnaise

1 tablespoons honey

1 ½ tablespoons lemon juice

1 tsp basil

1 tablespoon apple cider vinegar

½ teaspoon ground black pepper

¼ teaspoon salt

1 garlic clove, minced

DIRECTIONS:

1. Whisk all dressing ingredients in a bowl until smooth and creamy.

2. Add all salad ingredients to a bowl and toss to evenly coat with dressing.

3. Refrigerate for 2-3 hours before serving.

CUCUMBER SALAD

INGREDIENTS:

2 cucumbers, peeled and sliced

½ cup red onion, sliced

2 tablespoons fresh cilantro, chopped

2 cups cherry tomatoes, sliced

Salt and pepper to taste

1 clove garlic, minced

Balsamic dressing, to taste

DIRECTIONS:

1. Add ingredients and gently toss to combine.
2. Refrigerate for at least one hour before serving.

CHICKPEA SALAD

INGREDIENTS:

1 avocado, cut into cubes

½ fresh lemon, juiced

1 can chickpeas (19 ounces), drained

¼ cup red onion, sliced

2 cups cherry tomatoes, sliced

2 cups cucumber, peeled and sliced

½ cup fresh cilantro, chopped

¾ cup celery, chopped

For the dressing:

¼ cup olive oil

2 tablespoons red wine vinegar

½ teaspoon cumin

Salt and pepper to taste

INSTRUCTIONS:

1. Add ingredients and gently toss to combine.
2. Refrigerate at least one hour before serving.

SALSA SALAD

INGREDIENTS:

Dressing

   1 clove garlic, minced

   1 ½ lemons, juiced about three tablespoons

   2 teaspoons salt

   ¼ teaspoon paprika

   ¼ cup olive oil

Salad

   1 cucumber peeled and chopped small

   1 orange bell pepper seeded and diced

   1 red bell pepper seeded and diced

   ½ onion finely chopped

   Salt and pepper to taste

   1 cup tomatoes chopped

   1 small avocado, halved, seeded, and diced

   ¼ cup fresh cilantro chopped

DIRECTIONS:

1. Make the dressing. Whisk the garlic, salt, lemon juice, and paprika together in a bowl. Gradually whisk in the olive oil, starting with a few drops and then adding the rest in a steady stream.

2. For the salad: Toss together the cucumbers both bell peppers and onions. Add the dressing and toss to coat evenly. Gently fold in the tomatoes, avocado, and cilantro. Adjust seasoning with salt and pepper, to taste, and serve.

CHOPPED MEXICAN SALAD

INGREDIENTS:

1 head romaine lettuce, chopped small

1 bell pepper, chopped small

1 medium cucumber, chopped small

1 small jicama, peeled and chopped small

½ medium onion, chopped small

2 cups cherry tomatoes, cut in half

1 ½ cups celery, chopped small

1 small beet, peeled and chopped small

½ cup fresh cilantro, chopped small

1 cup sliced almonds

Balsamic dressing, to taste

INSTRUCTIONS:

1. Combine salad ingredients in a large bowl. Stir to combine.
2. Add dressing and stir to coat all ingredients to desired taste.
3. Chill before serving.

AVOCADO SPINACH SALAD WITH BALSAMIC DRESSING

INGREDIENTS:

6 cups fresh baby spinach

1pint strawberries, hulled and sliced

1 avocado, peeled, pitted and diced

4 ounces of goat cheese, shredded

¼ cup sliced almonds

Half a small red onion, thinly sliced

FOR THE DRESSING:

¼ cup balsamic vinegar

¼ cup olive oil

1 tablespoons honey

2 teaspoons yellow mustard

½ teaspoon basil

1 garlic clove, minced

Salt and pepper to taste

DIRECTIONS FOR THE SALAD:

1. Toss all ingredients together with your desired amount of dressing until combined.
2. Serve immediately

FOR THE DRESSING:

1. Combine ingredients into a pint mason jar and shake thoroughly.

_____

_____

_____

_____

_____

_____

_____

_____

_____

_____

_____

_____

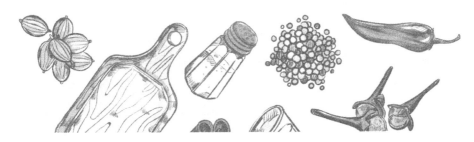

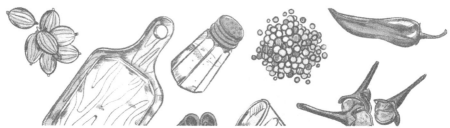

_____

_____

_____

_____

_____

_____

_____

_____

_____

_____

_____

_____

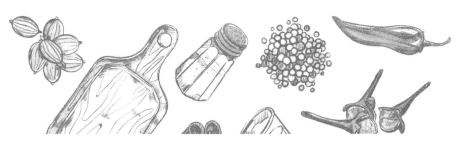

_____

_____

_____

_____

_____

_____

_____

_____

_____

_____

_____

_____

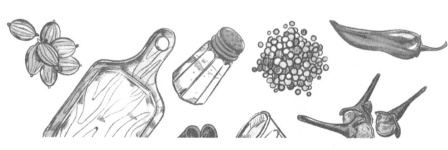

4

Dinner Recipes

"Dinner is where the magic happens in the kitchen."
~Kris Carr

"Seasonings should not begin and end at salt and pepper. Herbs and spices not only are a great source of variety but also add to the nutritional profile of a meal. Fresh or dried basil, oregano, cinnamon, cumin, nutmeg, and dozens of other herbs and spices are available in any well-stocked grocery store."
~Dr. William Davis

"Dinner is to a day what dessert is to dinner."
~Michael Dorris

MEATLOAF

INGREDIENTS:

1 ½ pounds hamburger meat (grass fed)

¾ cup oatmeal, uncooked (not quick cook oats)

1 cup dairy free milk, unsweetened and unflavored

1 egg

1 onion, chopped

2 tsp salt

¼ tsp pepper

1 tbsp. Worcestershire sauce

½ tsp dry mustard

1 tsp paprika

1-2 cloves of garlic, crushed

¼ tsp. sage

1 tbsp fresh thyme (or ½ tsp dried)

DIRECTIONS:

1. Mix all of the ingredients together.
2. spread in a greased 9x13 pan.
3. cook uncovered at 375 degrees until done, about 1-1 ½ hours.

SIMPLE BEEF DINNER

INGREDIENTS:

1 onion, chopped

1 teaspoon salt

2 pounds ground beef

4 cloves garlic, minced

1 medium tomato, chopped

2 tablespoons fresh cilantro, chopped

1 ½ teaspoons ground cumin

½ teaspoon chili powder

3 cups spinach, chopped

1 tablespoon fresh basil, chopped

¾ cup pimento-stuffed green or black olives

2 tablespoons coconut oil

2 stalks of celery, chopped

8 ounces tomato sauce

2 teaspoons red wine or apple cider vinegar

DIRECTIONS:

heat about a tablespoon of coconut or avocado oil in a large saute pan. Add the onion and saute until it softens, about 2-3 minutes. Add the ground meat and saute until the meat loses its raw red color. Add the remaining ingredients and stir to combine. Simmer until sauce thickens, about 5-10 minutes. Serve over squash noodles or brown rice.

BEEF COLLARD SOUP

INGREDIENTS:

1 ½ pounds stew meat, sliced into ¼ inch pieces

½ bundle of collard greens, finely chopped

½ bundle of kale, finely chopped

1 cup of salsa

2 large sweet potatoes, peeled and chopped

1 turnip, chopped

3 celery stalks, chopped

1 large onion, chopped

2 cloves garlic, minced

1 cup mushrooms, chopped

½ cup fresh parsley, chopped

6 small tomatoes, chopped

1 cup peas, frozen

3 teaspoons salt

¼ cup uncured pork bacon fat

½ teaspoon pepper

1-½ quarts chicken or bone broth

DIRECTIONS:

1. Add all ingredients into a large stew pot.
2. Cook on medium-high until a soft boil, then turn down to simmer.
3. Simmer softly for 1 to 1-½ hours, until meat is tender.
4. Add salt and pepper to taste.

BEEF AND RICE SKILLET

INGREDIENTS:

1 ¼ pounds ground beef (grass fed)

1 cup long grain white rice

2 ¼ cups chicken or beef broth

10 ounces of canned diced tomatoes with green chilies, undrained

1 red bell pepper, chopped

1 yellow squash, chopped

8 ounces goat cheese, grated

½ cup leeks, chopped

½ cup onion, chopped

¼ cup fresh cilantro, chopped

Salt and pepper, to taste

DIRECTIONS:

1. Cook ground beef, onion, leeks, squash, and bell pepper until meat is no longer pink.

2. Add rice, broth, spices, and canned tomatoes into the skillet with meat and vegetables and turn the heat up to high to bring to a boil. Cover with a lid and turn the heat down to just below medium. You want the dish to be at a constant, yet gentle, simmer. Simmer for 15-20 minutes, or until rice is tender, giving the mixture a quick stir about halfway through.

3. Once rice is tender, remove skillet form heat then stir in the cheese.

CROCK POT STEW

INGREDIENTS:

2 pounds beef chuck roast, fat trimmed, cut into 1-2 inch cubes

1 medium onion, chopped

2 stalks celery, chopped

6 carrots, sliced

½ cup tomato juice

3 teaspoons salt

2 cloves garlic, minced

6-8 cups Bone Broth (or chicken broth)

3 cups squash, zucchini, or sweet potatoes

1 tsp. black pepper

¼ cup fresh basil

1 tsp. turmeric

1 bay leaf

INSTRUCTIONS:

1. Place all ingredients into a crock pot.
2. Cook on high for 6-8 hours until desired tenderness.

HAMBURGER HASH

INGREDIENTS:

1lbs. hamburger meat

1 medium onion, chopped

3 eggs

1 tbsp. coconut oil

1lb.fresh spinach

2 tbsp. fresh cilantro

2 tbsp. fresh parsley

2 cloves of garlic, minced

Salt and pepper, to taste

DIRECTIONS:

1. Heat oil in skillet, then saute hamburger meat, onion, and garlic, Continue cooking until the meat browns and it loses its pink color.

2. Add spinach, cilantro, and parsley and stir until wilted, about 2-3 minutes.

3. Add salt and pepper.

4. In a separate bowl, whisk the eggs together.

5. Pour the eggs into the center of the pan and cook slightly before stirring everything together.

6. Continue cooking until eggs are done, to desired texture.

SLOW COOKED BEEF TIPS

INGREDIENTS:

3 pounds stew meat or top sirloin, cubed

2-3 tablespoons coconut oil

1 cup onion, chopped

1 bay leaf

3 cloves garlic, minced

4 cups beef or bone broth

2 teaspoons salt

Pepper, to taste

1 teaspoon paprika

1 tablespoon Worcestershire

1 teaspoon thyme

1 teaspoon oregano

¼ cup flour (gluten free)

INSTRUCTIONS:

1. Heat oil in a large skillet over medium-high heat.
2. Add beef and cook just long enough to sear the beef without cooking it through. Transfer beef to the slow cooker.
3. Place onions and bay leaf in the slow cooker.
4. In a small bowl add garlic, broth, salt, pepper, paprika, Worcestershire, thyme, oregano, and then whisk in the flour. Pour liquid over the beef.
5. Cover and cook on low for 7-8 hours or on high for 4-5 hours, or until beef is fork tender.
6. Serve over rice, mashed potatoes, or egg noodles

BAKED MEATBALLS

INGREDIENTS:

1 ½ pounds ground beef (grass fed is best)

1/3 cup goat cheese

¼ cup fresh oregano, finely chopped

2-3 tablespoons coconut oil

2 teaspoons salt

½ teaspoon pepper

1 teaspoon paprika

1 clove garlic, minced

1 teaspoon onion powder

2 eggs

DIRECTIONS:

1. Preheat oven to 375 degrees.
2. Grease baking sheet.
3. Add all ingredients into a large bowl and mix until well combined.
4. Roll into small meatballs and place on baking sheets.
5. Bake for 12-15 minutes or until internal temperature reaches 165 degrees.

CHICKEN CURRY

INGREDIENTS:

1-pound boneless, skinless chicken thighs

1 tbsp. coconut oil

2 garlic cloves minced

1 onion

1 red bell pepper

2-3 carrots peeled and sliced thin

2 15oz cans full fat coconut milk

½ cup chicken broth

Salt and pepper to taste

2 tbsp. curry powder

4 cups cooked rice

DIRECTIONS:

1. Heat the oil in a large pot over medium heat. Add the onion, garlic, bell pepper, and carrots, and cook for a few minutes until the onions are softened.

2. Add the chicken and cook chicken until it browns a little.

3. Add the coconut oil, salt, pepper, and curry powder and let simmer for 15-20 minutes or until the chicken is fully cooked.

4. Add chicken broth depending on the consistency you want or let simmer longer to thicken if desired.

5. Serve over cooked rice.

Optional: this could be served over spaghetti squash or eaten just as it is.

Vegetable option: omit the chicken and add one cup each of chopped squash and zucchini.

EASY ROASTED CHICKEN

INGREDIENTS:

3.5-4 pounds whole chicken, giblets removed

Salt and pepper to taste

Coconut oil (to rub over chicken)

Garlic powder (to sprinkle)

Oregano (to sprinkle)

DIRECTIONS:

1. Preheat oven to 450 degrees.
2. Rinse chicken inside and out with cool water then pat entire chicken, inside and out, dry with paper towels.
3. Rub coconut oil over entire chicken.
4. Season chicken generously with salt, a little bit of pepper, oregano and garlic, inside and out.
5. Tuck wings underneath the bird and place the chicken breast-side up on a roasting pan then roast until the skin is a deep golden brown on top, about 25-30 minutes.
6. Reduce heat to 400 degrees and continue roasting until the chicken is evenly browned and cooked through, about 25-40 additional minutes.
7. Insert a thermometer into the thickest part of the thigh, it should read 165 degrees. Let chicken rest for about 10 minutes before cutting.

CHICKEN TENDERS

INGREDIENTS:

2 Pounds chicken breast (boneless and skinless)

3 eggs

1 box gluten-free crackers

DIRECTIONS:

1. Preheat oven to 375 degrees. Spray a baking sheet with olive oil or avocado oil.

2. If your chicken is not already cut into chicken tenders, cut your chicken breast into chicken tender-like strips.

3. Add your whole grain crackers into a food processor and blend until your crackers become a fine powder. Pour into a large Ziplock bag.

4. Beat the 3 eggs.

5. Dip each chicken tender in the egg, and then drop into bag with crumbs, and shake until coated. Place on cookie sheet.

6. Bake the chicken tenders for 35-40 minutes, making sure to flip halfway through.

HOMEMADE HONEY MUSTARD

INGREDIENTS:

¼ cup raw honey

¼ cup plain yellow mustard

DIRECTIONS:

1. Mix together the raw honey and the plain yellow mustard until evenly combined. It may be a tad runny, so refrigerate if you would like it a bit thicker. Enjoy!

OVEN ROASTED BRISKET

INGREDIENTS:

6 pounds beef brisket, slightly trimmed

2 tbsp salt

2 tbsp paprika

2 tbsp chili powder

1 tbsp garlic powder

1 tbsp onion powder

2 tsp coriander

1 tsp black pepper

2 tsp dry mustard

2 tbsp Worcestershire sauce

2 tbsp apple cider vinegar

2 tbsp liquid smoke

INSTRUCTIONS:

1. Let's start 24 hours before cooking. Rinse brisket and pat it dry with paper towels. Rub into the meat half the Worcestershire and vinegar on each side of the meat.

2. Make a dry rub by combining all the dry spices.

3. Season the meat on both sides with the dry rub. Pat the rub well into the meat. Place into a roasting pan. Cover with foil and place into the fridge for 24-48 hours.

4. Preheat the oven to 350 degrees F.

5. Roast uncovered for 1 ½ hours.

6. Add enough water and liquid smoke to yield about a ½ inch of liquid in the roasting pan.

7. Lower the oven to 300 degrees F, cover pan tightly and continue cooking for 3 ½ hours, or until fork-tender.

8. Slice meat thinly across the grain. Top with the juice from the pan and serve warm.

FISH FLORENTINE

INGREDIENTS:

1 ½ pounds of fish fillets (wild caught)

3 tablespoons coconut oil

2 cups red bell pepper, chopped

2 cloves garlic, minced

12 ounces fresh spinach

½ cup plain dairy free yogurt

½ can full fat coconut milk (solid part)

½ cup goat cheese, grated

½ teaspoon dried parsley

Salt and pepper, to taste

INSTRUCTIONS:

1. Heat two tablespoons of oil in a large skillet over medium-high heat and add the fish. Sprinkle with salt and pepper. Cook the fish for 4-6 minutes on each side until cooked through. Turn off and cover.

2. Heat remaining oil in a separate skillet over medium-high heat. Add bell pepper and garlic and cook for 3-4 minutes.

3. Add the spinach and cook until wilted while stirring occasionally.

4. Add yogurt, milk, cheese, parsley, salt, and pepper and bring this to a gentle simmer, making sure that the cheese has completely melted, and is mixed in.

5. Gently transfer fish to skillet with spinach. Serve hot

IMMUNE BOOSTING SOUP

INGREDIENTS:

3 tablespoons coconut oil

2 pounds skinless boneless dark chicken (cut into 1-inch cubes)

1 onion, chopped

2 cloves garlic, minced

2 medium sweet potatoes, cubed

4 carrots, sliced

2 celery stalks, sliced

1 small bell pepper, chopped

2 small yellow squash, chopped

1 tablespoon fresh ginger, grated

1 tablespoon fresh turmeric, grated

2-3 teaspoons salt

Pepper, to taste

¼ cup fresh cilantro, chopped

¼ cup fresh parsley, chopped

6 cups chicken broth

3 cups spinach

INSTRUCTIONS:

1. In a large stockpot, heat oil and add chicken, onion, and garlic and cook on medium/high heat for 4-5 minutes.

2. Then add sweet potatoes, carrots, celery, and bell pepper and cook another 2-3 minutes.

3. Next add squash, ginger, turmeric, salt, pepper, cilantro, parsley, and broth in pan and stir.

4. Bring to a boil, cover, and simmer 45-50 minutes, until vegetables are tender.

5. Turn off heat and stir in spinach. Give the spinach 1-2 minutes to wilt.

6. Season with additional salt, if needed.

OPTIONAL: Add a spoon full of sauerkraut to bowls before serving!

BEEFY VEGETABLE CASSEROLE

INGREDIENTS:

1-pound grass fed ground beef

1 ½ cups of goat cheese

1 red bell pepper, chopped

1 yellow squash, chopped

1 yellow onion, chopped

1 cup cherry tomatoes, cut in half

1/3 Jalapeno Pepper, chopped

1 TBSP Chili Powder

2 TSP Coriander Powder

1 TSP cumin

1 TSP garlic powder

2 TSP paprika

1 bag of fresh oregano, chopped

2 TSP salt

1 head of broccoli florets

Half a head (3-4 leaves) of kale, torn into small pieces

5 red potatoes, sliced like chips

DIRECTIONS:

1. Combine beef, bell pepper, onion, spices, and jalapeno pepper into a saucepan and cook until your meat is no longer pink. Set aside

2. Then take the red potatoes, kale, broccoli, and squash and layer them into a casserole dish in order.

3. Next add the ingredients from the saucepan into the casserole dish.

4. Layer the top with the diced tomatoes and cheese.

5. Bake at 375 degrees for 45-50 minutes.

ZUCCHINI LASAGNA

INGREDIENTS:

1 lb. ground beef

1 small onion, diced

1 tablespoon coconut oil

4 large zucchinis

1 (24oz) jar pasta sauce

5 large basil leaves, chopped

½ cup fresh cilantro, chopped

¼ cup fresh parsley, chopped

1 container of plain almond yogurt

2 ½ cups goat or sheep cheese

1 teaspoon garlic powder

Salt and pepper, to taste

DIRECTIONS:

1. Preheat oven to 375. Lightly grease a 9X13 casserole pan.

2. In a large pot over medium-high heat, heat oil. Cook ground beef and onion until meat is no longer pink.

3. Thinly slice two of the zucchinis and place into the casserole pan, covering the bottom of the pan. Sprinkle with salt, pepper, and ½ of the garlic powder. Top with beef mixture.

4. Spread yogurt and pasta sauce over meat, covering completely.

5. Sprinkle basil, cilantro, parsley, remaining garlic powder, salt, and pepper if desired.

6. Top with remaining zucchinis diced into small pieces. Sprinkle with cheese. Bake for about 45-50 minutes.

ROASTED CHICKEN AND VEGETABLES

INGREDIENTS:

1 lb. brussels sprouts, trimmed and halved

1 lb. sweet potatoes, cut into bite-sized pieces

½ red onion, chopped

¼ cup avocado oil

2 tablespoons honey

¼ cup gluten free soy sauce

¼ cup fresh cilantro, chopped

1 ½ lbs. chicken thighs (boneless and skinless)

¼ cup balsamic dressing

1 clove garlic, minced

Salt and pepper, to taste

¼ cup fresh parsley, chopped

½ teaspoon paprika

DIRECTIONS:

1. Preheat oven to 450 degrees. Lightly grease a baking sheet pan.

2. Combine the brussels sprouts, sweet potatoes, onion, oil, honey, soy sauce, and parsley in a large bowl. Toss to combine. Spread veggie mixture onto baking sheet.

3. Combine chicken, balsamic dressing, garlic, salt, pepper, parsley, and paprika. Toss to combine.

4. Arrange chicken on top of the veggies.

5. Bake for 40-50 minutes or until chicken and veggies are cooked through.

BEEF CABBAGE DISH

INGREDIENTS:

1 ½ pounds ground beef

1 onion, chopped

2 cloves garlic, minced

1 small head of cabbage, chopped

2 tbsp coconut oil

¾ cup white rice

Salt and pepper, to taste

2 carrots, peeled and sliced thin

1 tsp cumin

1 tsp dried dill

3 tbsp fresh parsley, chopped small

2 (14.5oz) cans diced tomatoes with liquid

1 (32oz) carton chicken broth

INSTRUCTIONS:

1. Heat oil in a large skillet over medium-high heat. Add onion, garlic, and ground beef and cook until no longer pink.

2. Stir in cabbage, rice, salt, pepper, carrots, cumin, dill, parsley, tomatoes, and broth until combined and bring to a light boil.

3. Reduce heat to a simmer, cover and let cook until rice is tender, about 15-20 minutes. Serve immediately.

SPAGHETTI SQUASH CASSEROLE

INGREDIENTS:

1 small/medium spaghetti squash (about 2 pounds)

2 teaspoons coconut oil

1-pound hamburger meat (grass fed)

1 stalk celery, chopped

1 small onion, diced

1 red bell pepper, cored and diced

¼ cup fresh cilantro

2 teaspoons salt

½ teaspoon black pepper

1 can (14.5 ounce) diced tomatoes, drained

3 cloves of garlic, minced

1 tsp oregano

1 tsp paprika

1 tsp basil

1 cup goat cheese

DIRECTIONS:

1. Preheat oven to 375°F.

2. Slice the squash in half, lengthwise, and scoop out the seeds.

3. Spray a baking sheet and the inside of the squash with oil. Place cut-side down on baking sheet and bake for 35 to 45 minutes, until the flesh of the squash is easily pierced with a fork. When cool enough to handle, pull the squash strings out of the squash's center with a fork.

4. Reduce the oven temperature to 350° F.

5. Heat oil in a large, deep skillet over medium high heat. Add the meat, onion, celery, bell pepper, salt, and black pepper, and cook until the meat is browned and the vegetables are tender, about 8 minutes.

6. Add the drained tomatoes, garlic, and spices and let it cook until most of the liquid from the tomatoes has cooked off, about 4 minutes.

7. Add ½ a cup of the shredded cheese and the squash to the skillet.

8. Lightly coat a 2-quart casserole dish with a nonstick spray. Add squash casserole and bake, uncovered, for 20 minutes.

9. Remove from the oven and sprinkle with the remaining ½ a cup of cheese and return to the oven, and bake until the cheese melts, about 5 to 10 additional minutes.

CREAMY BEEF OVER RICE

INGREDIENTS:

2 lbs grass fed beef (cutlets or fajita)

8 large carrots, peeled and cut into rounds

1 medium onion, chopped

6 stalks celery, chopped

3 cloves garlic, minced

2 teaspoons salt

½ teaspoon pepper

½ cup fresh parsley, chopped

1 teaspoon turmeric

1 teaspoon paprika

1 can full-fat coconut milk

1 cup chicken broth

DIRECTIONS:

1. Place beef in the bottom of the slow cooker, then add carrots, onion, celery, garlic, salt, pepper, parsley, turmeric, and paprika.
2. Pour the coconut milk and broth over vegetables.
3. Cook on high for 5 hours or low for 9-10 hours.
4. Serve over rice.

MEXICAN BEEF DISH

INGREDIENTS:

1 onion, chopped

1 teaspoon salt

2 pounds ground beef

4 cloves garlic, minced

1 medium tomato, chopped

2 tablespoons fresh cilantro, chopped

1 ½ teaspoons ground cumin

½ teaspoon chili powder

3 cups spinach, chopped

1 tablespoon fresh basil, chopped

¾ cup pimento-stuffed green or black olives

2 tablespoons coconut oil

2 stalks of celery, chopped

8 ounces tomato sauce

2 teaspoons red wine or apple cider vinegar

DIRECTIONS:

heat about a tablespoon of coconut or avocado oil in a large saute pan. Add the onion and saute until it softens, about 2-3 minutes. Add the ground meat and saute until the meat loses its raw red color. Add the remaining ingredients and stir to combine. Simmer until sauce thickens, about 5-10 minutes. Serve over squash noodles or brown rice.

SWEET POTATO CASSEROLE

INGREDIENTS:

3 cups cooked and mashed
    sweet potatoes

3 tbsp coconut oil, melted

1 tsp vanilla

2 eggs

¼ cup maple syrup

¼ tsp. baking soda

1 tsp cinnamon

DIRECTIONS:

1. Place all ingredients into a large mixing bowl.
2. Mix until fluffy.
3. Place into greased 9x13 pan

TOPPING

¾ cup maple syrup

1 cup pecans, chopped small

1 cup shredded unsweetened
    coconut

¼ cup coconut oil, melted

½ cup gluten free flour

DIRECTIONS:

1. Mix all ingredients in a large bowl.
2. Layer on top of sweet potatoes.
3. Bake at 350°for 30-40 minutes.

MASHED YELLOW SQUASH

INGREDIENTS:

4-6 yellow squash (cut into cubes)

¼ cup coconut oil

Salt and pepper to taste

1 tsp. oregano

½ tsp. paprika

DIRECTIONS:

Place squash into pot with about one inch of water. Cover and bring to a boil, then turn down to low/medium and boil till soft. Drain water. Mash like mash potatoes. Drain again, and add oil and spices.

BACON BRUSSELS SPROUTS

INGREDIENTS:

3 slices bacon, chopped small

9oz Bag whole brussels sprouts

1-2 tablespoons coconut oil (add more if needed, while cooking)

1 cloves garlic, minced

Salt and pepper to taste

1 teaspoon dried basil

OPTIONAL: Drizzle with maple syrup

DIRECTIONS:

Add bacon to skillet. Cook on medium until bacon begins to sizzle. Add coconut oil, garlic, basil and brussels sprouts. Saute stirring occasionally, until the brussels sprouts and bacon are golden brown about 10-15 minutes. Season with salt and pepper. You can drizzle with a little olive oil for extra flavor.

KALE

INGREDIENTS:

½ pounds young kale leaves, coarsely chopped (stems removed)

2 tablespoons coconut oil

2 cloves garlic, finely sliced

¼ cup onion (cut small)

½ cup vegetable stock (or water)

Salt and pepper, to taste

2 tablespoons red wine vinegar

DIRECTIONS:

1. Heat oil in a large saucepan over medium heat.
2. Add the garlic and onion and cook until soft, but not colored.
3. Raise heat to medium/high, add the stock and kale stir to combine.
4. Cover and cook for five minutes.
5. Remove cover and continue to cook, stirring until all the liquid has evaporated.
6. Season with salt and pepper to taste and add vinegar.
7. Optional: Drizzle with olive oil for extra flavor

CARROTS

INGREDIENTS:

2 pounds carrots (peeled and sliced)

¼ cup oil or dairy free butter

Salt and pepper to taste

½ tsp. garlic powder

1 tsp paprika

1 tsp. parsley

Equal parts chicken broth and water

DIRECTIONS:

Place the carrots in a crock pot. Add oil and spices. Add chicken broth and water to cover carrots. Cook on HIGH for 3 hours or until carrots are tender.

ZUCCHINI

INGREDIENTS:

4-6 zucchini—cut into ½ inch slices

2-3 tbs coconut oil

Salt and pepper to taste

1 tsp oregano

½ tsp garlic powder

DIRECTIONS:

1. Preheat oven to 425 degrees.
2. Toss zucchini with oil and spices.
3. Place in a single layer on a greased baking sheet.
4. Bake for 10-15 minutes, the zucchini should be tender/crisp.

Optional: sprinkle with nutritional yeast if you want a cheesy flavor!

BAKED SWEET POTATOES

DIRECTIONS:

1. Scrub and wash sweet potatoes.
2. Stab unpeeled potatoes five or six times with fork
3. Spray crock pot and outside of potatoes with oil.
4. Place in crock pot and cook on high for 5-6 hours or until tender

MASHED SWEET POTATOES

DIRECTIONS:

1. Peel, wash, and cut up potatoes in cubes
2. Spray crock pot with oil, add cubed sweet potatoes, and cook on high for 5-6 hours
3. Mash potatoes, add coconut oil or dairy free butter, and cinnamon, to taste.

BOK CHOY

INGREDIENTS:

Bok Choy cut into bite sized pieces

3 tbs. coconut oil

2 cloves garlic (crushed)

¼ cup onion, chopped

¼ cup Fresh cilantro, chopped

Salt & pepper, to taste

DIRECTIONS:

1. Heat the oil in a large skillet; cook the garlic and onion in the hot oil until fragrant, 2-3 minutes.

2. Mix in the Bok Choy and cilantro and cook and stir until the green parts of the leaves turn bright green and the stalks become slightly translucent, 5 to 10 minutes. Sprinkle with salt and pepper. Drizzle with olive oil. Enjoy!

ROASTED BROCCOLI

INGREDIENTS:

1 head broccoli (separated into florets)

2 tbsp. coconut oil, melted

1-2 tsp. salt

½ tsp black pepper

¼ tsp. garlic powder

½ tsp. basil

DIRECTIONS:

1. Preheat the oven to 400 degrees.
2. In a large bowl, toss broccoli florets with oil, salt, pepper, basil, and garlic.
3. Spread the broccoli out in an even layer on a greased baking sheet.
4. Bake in the preheated oven until florets are tender enough to pierce the stems with a fork, 18 to 25 minutes.
5. Remove and transfer to a serving platter.
6. Drizzle with olive oil for flavor.

ROASTED CAULIFLOWER

INGREDIENTS:

1 head cauliflower (separated into florets)

2 cloves garlic, minced

3 tbsp coconut oil

Salt and pepper to taste

2 tbsp fresh thyme, chopped or ½ tsp. ground thyme

DIRECTIONS:

1. Preheat oven to 450 degrees Fahrenheit. Grease a large casserole dish.

2. Place the oil, garlic, and thyme into a large resealable bag. Add cauliflower and shake to mix. Pour into prepared casserole dish, and season with salt, and pepper.

3. Bake for 25 minutes, stirring halfway through.

Optional: you could add nutritional yeast or raw goat cheese on top to give a cheesy flavor.

CABBAGE

INGREDIENTS:

1 head of cabbage (cut up)

2tbsp. coconut or olive oil

Salt, to taste

Black pepper, to taste

1 tbsp cumin

DIRECTIONS:

1. Place the cabbage into a large pot with an inch of water.
2. Cover and bring to a boil.
3. Reduce heat to medium and cook for 5-10 minutes after the boiling begins until desired tenderness.
4. Drain and add oil and spices.

ZUCCHINI SPINACH CASSEROLE

INGREDIENTS:

2 Tbsp coconut oil

3 cups baby spinach

4 small zucchini, diced small

4 small yellow squash, diced small

1 cup goat cheese, grated

3 tbsp ground flaxseed

2 eggs

2 garlic cloves, minced

2 tsp salt

¼ tsp black pepper

2 tbsp fresh basil, chopped

½ tsp sage

INSTUCTIONS:

1. Preheat the oven to 400 degrees.
2. Grease a 9x13 casserole dish and set aside.
3. In a large skillet, heat oil and add the spinach, zucchini, and squash. Cook 3-5 minutes, until the squash is soft.
4. Drain off liquid and place into a large bowl. Add remaining ingredients and combine well. Spread into prepared dish.
5. Bake for 30-40 minutes.

STEAMED ASPARAGUS

INGREDIENTS:

1 bundle of asparagus

2 tbsp coconut oil or dairy free butter

Salt and black pepper, to taste

1 garlic clove, minced

2 tsp parsley

DIRECTIONS:

1. Fill a medium saucepan halfway with lightly salted water.
2. Bring to a boil.
3. While the water is heating, prepare the asparagus. Rinse them thoroughly; break off any tough, white bottoms and discard.
4. Cut the spears into 1 to 2 inch sections.
5. Add the asparagus to the boiling water and lower the heat slightly to maintain a simmer. Boil asparagus for 2-3 minutes. Do not over cook.
6. Drain the hot water
7. Toss with the oil, and spices.
8. Salt and pepper to taste.

SPAGHETTI SQUASH

INGREDIENTS:

1 medium spaghetti squash

1 tsp oregano

2 tsp salt

½ tsp pepper

1 cup spinach, chopped fine (raw)

1 tsp garlic powder

¼ cup fresh cilantro, chopped

Drizzle with olive oil, until desired taste

DIRECTIONS:

1. Preheat oven to 375° Fahrenheit
2. Slice the squash in half, lengthwise, and scoop out the seeds
3. Grease pan and the inside of the squash with oil
4. Place cut-side down on baking pan.
5. Bake for 35-45 minutes or until the flesh of the squash is easily pierced with a fork.
6. Pull the squash strings out of the squash's center with a fork.
7. Place squash noodles in a large bowl.
8. Add oregano, salt, pepper, spinach, garlic, cilantro, and olive oil.
9. Mix well (the heat from the squash will soften the spinach and cilantro without cooking.)

OPTIONAL:

ADD chicken, beef, sautéed onion, or bell peppers.

_____

_____

_____

_____

_____

_____

_____

_____

_____

_____

_____

_____

_____

_____

_____

_____

_____

_____

_____

_____

_____

_____

_____

_____

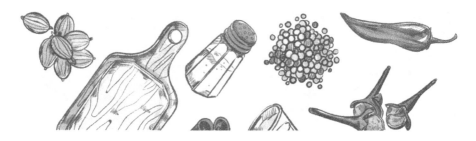

_____

_____

_____

_____

_____

_____

_____

_____

_____

_____

_____

_____

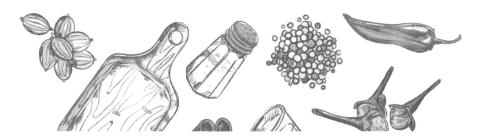

_____

_____

_____

_____

_____

_____

_____

_____

_____

_____

_____

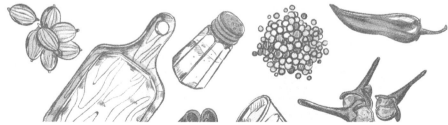

_____

_____

_____

_____

_____

_____

_____

_____

_____

_____

_____

_____

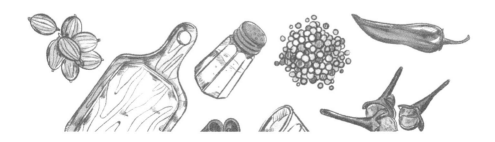

_____

_____

_____

_____

_____

_____

_____

_____

_____

_____

_____

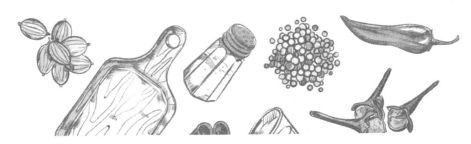

5

Dessert Recipes

"The proof of the pudding is in the eating."
~William Camden

"Berries (blueberries, blackberries, strawberries, cranberries, cherries) are at the top of the list with the greatest nutrient content and the least sugars, while bananas, pineapple, mango, and papaya need to be especially limited due to high sugar content."
~William Davis

"Desserts are the fairy tales of the kitchen—a happily-ever-after to supper."
~Terri Guillemets

PUMPKIN CREAM PIE

INGREDIENTS:

1 gluten free graham pie crust (or homemade)

1-16oz. non-dairy whipped topping (So Delicious)

1 can pumpkin

1 tablespoon pumpkin spice

½ teaspoon cinnamon

Dash of salt

2 boxes vanilla pudding

DIRECTIONS:

1. Combine half of the whipped topping, with pumpkin, pumpkin spice, cinnamon, salt, and pudding powder.
2. Blend with hand mixer on medium until fluffy.
3. Add to pie crust.
4. Top with remaining whipped topping and sprinkle with pumpkin spice.
5. Chill in refrigerator for 6 hours or overnight. Best kept in the refrigerator.

OATMEAL BANANA BARS

INGREDIENTS:

1 cup ripe mashed banana

½ cup maple syrup

2 tablespoons melted coconut oil

2 teaspoons vanilla extract

1 egg

¼ cup gluten free flour blend

2 tablespoons ground flaxseed

½ teaspoon baking soda

¼ teaspoon salt

½ teaspoon cinnamon

1 cup quick oats

1 cup raisins

DIRECTIONS:

1. Preheat oven to 350° and grease an 8x8 baking pan.
2. Whisk together the banana, maple syrup, oil, vanilla, and egg, until well blended.
3. Mix together the flour, flaxseed, baking soda, salt, cinnamon, oats, and raisins in separate bowl.
4. Stir in the dry mixture with the wet until combined.
5. Bake 30 minutes.

RAW FIG DELIGHTS

INGREDIENTS:

3 cups dried figs, stems removed

1 cup cashews

1 tablespoon vanilla extract

1 tsp orange zest

½ teaspoon salt

¼ tsp cinnamon

DIRECTIONS:

1. Place all ingredients in food processor and blend on low until chopped and mixture starts to stick together. Go from low to high on processor until its done.

2. Form into small round balls between your hands.

3. Enjoy at room temperature, refrigerate, or even freeze them (just taking them out of the freezer about 5 minutes before eating).

DAIRY FREE FUDGE

INGREDIENTS:

2 (11.25oz) cans of Sweetened Condensed Coconut Milk

1 tbsp coconut oil

Pinch of salt

1 tbsp vanilla

¾ heaping cup pecans, chopped

3 ¾ cups dairy free semi-sweet chocolate chips (I used Enjoy Life)

DIRECTIONS:

1. Line a 9x9 pan with lightly oiled parchment paper.
2. Put the milk, oil and chocolate chips into a large glass bowl and microwave on high for 1 minute. Stir vigorously. Microwave in 30-second intervals. Stirring well each time, until the chocolate is melted.
3. Stir in the salt, vanilla, and pecans until well combined.
4. Pour the mixture into the prepared pan.
5. Refrigerate for 3 hours or until set. Best if kept refrigerated.

CINNAMON RAISIN PROTEIN BALLS

INGREDIENTS:

1 ½ cups old-fashion rolled oats

1 cup creamy cashew butter

3 tbsp honey

1 scoop chocolate protein powder

½ cup raisins

½ tsp vanilla

½ tsp cinnamon

DIRECTIONS:

1. Place all ingredients into food processor and blend well.
2. Roll into bite size balls.
3. Best if chilled first. Store in the refrigerator or freezer.

OPTIONAL: Melt 4 tablespoons of semi-sweet chocolate chips (I used Enjoy Life). Dip one side of the ball into the chocolate.

PEANUT BUTTER BALLS

INGREDIENTS:

1 ½ cup old fashion rolled oats

1 cup creamy peanut butter

3 tablespoons honey

1 scoop vanilla protein powder

½ cup raisins

½ teaspoon vanilla

½ teaspoon cinnamon

5 tablespoons semi-sweet chocolate chips (I used Enjoy Life).

DIRECTIONS:

1. Place all ingredients into a food processor and blend well.
2. Roll into bite size balls.
3. Melt chocolate chips.
4. Dip one side of the ball into the chocolate and place into the refrigerator to harden.
5. Store in the refrigerator or freezer.

PECAN PIE

INGREDIENTS:

1 (9 inch) gluten free pie crust

1 cup raw brown sugar

1 cup of brown rice syrup

3 large eggs

2 tsp vanilla

Pinch of salt

¼ cup dairy free butter, melted

2 cups shelled pecans

DIRECTIONS:

1. Preheat oven to 350°.
2. Put all of the ingredients in a bowl. Mix with a fork until combined. Pour into the pie crust.
3. Bake on center rack of oven for 55-65 minutes or until knife inserted into the center of the pie comes out clean. Cool for a couple hours before cutting.

CRUNCH BALLS

INGREDIENTS:

1 CUP DATES

¾ CUP CASHEWS

1 ½ CUPS PECANS

2 TBSP COCOA POWDER

1 CUP UNSWEETENED FINE SHREDDED COCONUT (FOR ROLLING)

¾ CUP CASHEW BUTTER

½ CUP RAISINS

2-4 TBSP ALMOND MILK

DIRECTIONS:

1. Place all ingredients (except coconut milk and the shredded coconut) into a food processor and pulse for 5 minutes, or until finely chopped, and sticky enough to hold their shape when rolled into balls.

2. Slowly add coconut milk until desired texture and moisture is achieved (optional).

3. Form even sized balls.

4. Then roll in shredded coconut.

5. Refrigerate until set. They taste better chilled.

BANANA PUDDING

INGREDIENTS:

1 large package of instant vanilla pudding

1 can (12.2 oz) evaporated coconut milk (I use Nature's Charm)

(for the remaining milk use vanilla almond milk)

1 tsp vanilla

2 containers of dairy free whip cream

1 can (11.25 oz) sweetened condensed coconut milk

Bananas, cut into ½ inch slices

2 boxes vanilla wafers (I use kinnikinnick)

DIRECTIONS:

1. Make the box of pudding using the can of evaporated coconut milk and almond milk

2. Leg stand for one hour in the refrigerator to firm the pudding.

3. Add the condensed milk, whip cream, and vanilla to the pudding and stir to lightly combine.

4. In a large bowl make one layer of wafers, covering the entire base of the bowl.

5. Top with banana slices covering the wafers.

6. Pour half the pudding mixture over the bananas, smoothing lightly with a spatula.

7. Repeat the layers of wafers, another layer of bananas, and top with remaining pudding, smoothing the top lightly with a spatula.

8. Cover and refrigerate the pudding for at least 4 hours, or overnight.

9. Serve garnished with crushed wafers and banana slices.

NUT BUTTER PROTEIN BALLS

INGREDIENTS:

1-½ cups pecans

1 scoop protein powder

½ scoop collagen

¾ cup raisins

2 teaspoons vanilla

2 teaspoons cinnamon

Pinch of salt

1 cup creamy nut butter

½ cup unsweetened shredded coconut

DIRECTIONS:

1. Place pecans in food processor and grind into fine powder.
2. Add the rest of the ingredients, expect the shredded coconut, and process until pasty.
3. Using your hands, roll into bite-sized balls, and then roll into a plate of shredded coconut to top.
4. Best kept in refrigerator or freezer.

OPTIONAL: you can roll into finely chopped nuts if you don't like coconut.

PUMPKIN PIE

INGREDIENTS:

1 gluten free pie crust

1 (15-oz) can pure pumpkin

1 (11.25-oz) can sweetened condensed coconut milk

2 tablespoons maple syrup

3 eggs

2 teaspoons pumpkin pie spice

¼ teaspoon salt

1 teaspoon vanilla

1 teaspoon cinnamon

Dash of cloves

DIRECTIONS:

1. Preheat oven to 425 degrees.
2. In a large bowl combine all ingredients and stir until smooth.
3. Pour into pie shell.
4. Bake for 15 minutes at 425 degrees. Reduce temperature to 350 degrees and bake for 45-55 minutes or until knife inserted near the center comes out clean.
5. Cool. Garnish as desired. Store leftovers covered in refrigerator.

EASY HOMEMADE SNACKBARS

INGREDIENTS:

1 ½ cups pitted medjool dates

¾ cup unsweetened shredded coconut

½ cup almonds or macadamias

½ cup cashews

Pinch of salt

1 tablespoons vanilla

Half of a red apple (peeled)

1/3 cup chocolate chips (I used Enjoy Life)

INSTRUCTIONS:

1. Line a 8x8 square pan with lightly greased parchment paper.
2. Place coconut, almonds, and cashews into food processor and pulse until they are chopped into small pieces.
3. Add dates, salt, vanilla, and apple into the processor with nuts. Process on low until well combined and sticky.
4. Add chocolate chips and pulse a few times, until they are just incorporated.
5. Remove mixture from processor and press evenly into your prepared pan. Press firmly so they will stick together.
6. Place in the refrigerator for a couple of hours or until they are hard enough to slice into bars. Best if kept in the refrigerator or freezer!

DAIRY FREE HOT CHOCOLATE

INGREDIENTS:

1 cup unsweetened vanilla almond milk

1 tbsp raw unsweetened cocoa powder

1 tbsp honey

1 tbsp dairy free semi sweet chocolate chips (I used Enjoy Life)

Dash of salt

1/8 tsp pure vanilla extract

¼ tsp coconut oil (or a good fat that slows down sugar spike

DIRECTIONS:

1. Place all ingredients into a small saucepan and whisk constantly over medium heat until it reaches a soft boil.

2. Taste and adjust sweetness, as needed.

3. Lastly, you could add peppermint extract or top with coconut whip cream.

PECAN BALLS

INGREDIENTS:

1 ½ cups pecans

1 cup dates or raisins

1 tsp vanilla

2 tsp cinnamon

¼ tsp salt

DIRECTIONS:

1. Blend pecans until they form a coarse flour.
2. Add other ingredients and process until mixture is sticky.
3. Using your hands roll mixture into balls.
4. Store at room temperature or place in freezer and remove a few minutes before eating.

OPTIONAL: Roll balls in unsweetened coconut or finely chopped nuts, so they want be sticky.

HOMEMADE DARK CHOCOLATE

INGREDIENTS:

½ CUP COCONUT OIL

½ CUP COCOA POWDER

3 Tbs. HONEY

½ TSP. VANILLA EXTRACT

½ CUP PECANS

1 PINCH SEA SALT

DIRECTIONS:

1. Gently melt coconut oil in a saucepan over medium-low heat.
2. Turn off.
3. Add remaining ingredients and stir well. (Do this step quickly)
4. Spray a bread loaf pan and pour mixture into pan.
5. Refrigerate at least an hour.
6. Keep in refrigerator. (Chocolate will soften at room temperature)

GRAHAM CRACKER CRUST
Gluten and dairy free

INGREDIENTS:

1 bag gluten free graham or animal crackers, 6 oz bag (ground finely in food processor) (I use Glutino) Yields one cup

3 ½ tbsp sugar

4 tbsp dairy free butter, melted (I used Earth Balance)

½ tsp cinnamon (optional)

Optional: substitute YOUR FAVORITE cookies

DIRECTIONS:

1. Mix graham cracker crumbs, sugar, butter, and cinnamon until well blended.
2. Press mixture into a lightly greased 8 or 9 inch pie plate.
3. Bake at 375°for 7 minutes.
4. Cool to room temp before using.

CARROT CAKE

DRY INGREDIENTS:

2 cups gluten free flour blend (I used Bob Mills)

2 cups sugar

1 ½ teaspoons baking powder

1 teaspoon baking soda

1 teaspoon cinnamon

¼ teaspoon nutmeg

½ teaspoon salt

1 cup shredded coconut

1 cup chopped pecans or walnuts

WET INGREDIENTS:

¾ cup melted coconut oil

½ cup unsweetened applesauce

4 eggs

1 teaspoon vanilla

¾ cup crushed pineapple (in its own juice)

2 cups grated carrots (peel first)

DIRECTIONS:

1. Combine dry ingredients in large mixing bowl and stir well.
2. Combine wet ingredients in large mixing bowl and stir well.
3. Combine dry and wet ingredients.
4. Pour into a greased 9x13 or two round cake pans
5. Bake for 35-45 minutes
6. Allow the cake to cool for 10-15 minutes in the pan before removing. Allow cake to cool completely before adding icing. I recommend the cashew icing.

CASHEW ICING

INGREDIENTS:

1 ¼ cups cashews

1 tablespoon melted coconut oil

Dash of salt

¼ cup can full fat coconut milk

¼ cup almond milk

3 tablespoons maple syrup

2 tablespoons lemon juice

1 teaspoon vanilla

DIRECTIONS:

1. Add all ingredients to blender, and blend till smooth.
2. Place in the refrigerator for a couple of hours. It will thicken as it cools.

LEMON PIE

INGREDIENTS:

½ cup fresh lemon juice (from 2 to 3 medium lemons)

4 cups dairy free whip cream divided (2 for pudding 2 for topping)

1 large box vanilla pudding

1 can sweetened coconut condensed milk

1 gluten free graham pie crust

DIRECTIONS:

1. In a medium bowl combine lemon juice, box pudding, and condensed milk and stir until well mixed.
2. Fold in 2 cups of whip cream.
3. Pour pudding mixture into pie crust.
4. Top with remaining whip cream'.
5. Chill in refrigerator for 2 hours before cutting.

RAW BROWNIES

INGREDIENTS:

1 CUP PECANS
1 CUP CASHEWS
1 CUP RAISINS
1 CUP DATES
6 TBSP COCAO POWDER
  OR CAROB POWDER

½ TBS GROUND FLAXSEED
1 TBS VANILLA
¼ TSP CINNAMON
1/8 TSP SALT

TOPPING

¼ CUP COCONUT OIL
¼ CUP HONEY
¼ CUP CACAO POWDER
  OR CAROB POWDER

¼ tsp VANILLA
DASH OF SALT

DIRECTIONS:

1. In a food processor, process the nuts, raisins, dates, cacao, flaxseed, vanilla, cinnamon, and salt until the mixture is chopped and starts to stick together.

2. Press into lightly greased 9 by 9 square pan

3. Put in freezer for 30 minutes

4. Make chocolate topping by melting the coconut oil and adding the honey, cacao powder, vanilla, and dash of salt. Do not over cook, just melt.

5. Pour chocolate over brownies in pan.

6. Keep in refrigerator or cut into small pieces and wrap with aluminum foil. Then place into freezer ziplock bag and place in freezer. Remove from freezer a few minutes before enjoying

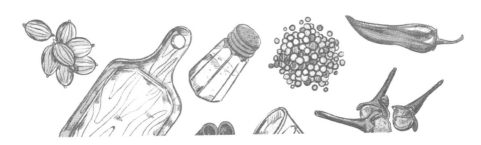

_____

_____

_____

_____

_____

_____

_____

_____

_____

_____

_____

_____

_____

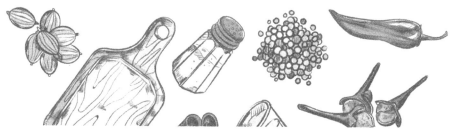

_____

_____

_____

_____

_____

_____

_____

_____

_____

_____

_____

_____

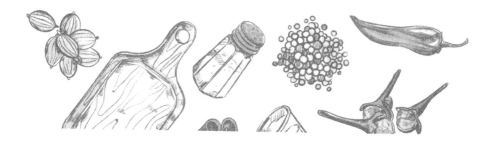

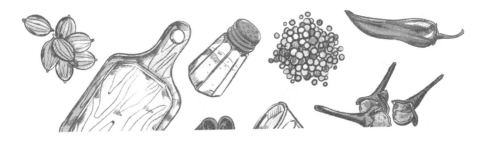

_____

_____

_____

_____

_____

_____

_____

_____

_____

_____

_____

_____

_____

_____

_____

_____

_____

_____

_____

_____

_____

_____

_____

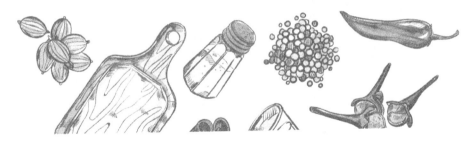

6

Bread Recipes

"All sorrows are less with bread."
~Miguel de Cervantes

"Laughter is brightest where food is the best."
~Irish proverb

"Without wishing in the slightest degree to disparage
the skill and labor of breadmakers by trade, truth
compels us to assert our conviction of the superior
wholesomeness of bread made in our own homes."
~Eliza Acton

GLUTEN FREE CORNBREAD

INGREDIENTS:

1 ½ cups organic cornmeal

½ cup gluten-free flour blend

2 tsp baking powder

1 tsp salt

½ tsp baking soda

1 tsp cider vinegar

2 eggs

¼ cup coconut oil, melted

1 ½ cups unsweetened almond milk

DIRECTIONS:

1. Preheat oven to 450 degrees.
2. Grease an 8x8x2 square pan
3. Combine all the dry ingredients in a bowl.
4. Add wet ingredients and mix well
5. Pour the batter into the prepared baking pan and bake for 25-30 minutes, or until a toothpick inserted in the center comes out clean.
6. Serve warm

GRAINFREE BREAD

INGREDIENTS:

2 CUPS FINE GROUND ALMOND FLOUR

½ CUP GROUND FLAXSEED

½ TEASPOON SALT

1 TEASPOON BAKING SODA

1 TEASPOON BAKING POWDER

½ CUP ARROWROOT POWDER

½ CUP COCONUT OIL, MELTED

5 LARGE EGGS

1 TEASPOON APPLE CIDER VINEGAR

½ CUP CANNED FULL FAT COCONUT MILK (use the cream and the liquid from the can)

DIRECTIONS:

1. Preheat oven to 350 degrees.
2. In a large bowl, mix the flour, flaxseed, salt, baking soda, baking powder, and arrowroot powder.
3. In another bowl, whisk together oil, eggs, vinegar, and milk.
4. Gently stir wet and dry ingredients until mixed, being careful not to over mix.
5. Pour batter into a medium loaf pan lined with greased parchment paper.
6. Bake 55-65 minutes or until a toothpick inserted into the center of the bread comes out clean.
7. Let it cool for ten minutes before removing from pan and parchment paper.
8. Place on wire rack until completely cooled.

OATMEAL BLUEBERRY MUFFINS

INGREDIENTS:

1 ¼ cups old-fashioned rolled oats (gluten free)

1 cup almond milk

1 cup gluten free flour blend

1 tablespoon baking powder

½ teaspoon salt

½ teaspoon cinnamon

¼ cup coconut oil, melted

½ cup maple syrup

1 egg

1 teaspoon vanilla

1 cup fresh blueberries, (if you use frozen do not thaw)

DIRECTIONS:

1. Preheat oven to 425 degrees. Line a 12-count muffin pan with cupcake liners.

2. Combine milk and oats. Set aside so the oats can soak up some moisture.

3. Whisk the flour, baking powder, salt, and cinnamon together in a large bowl until combined. Sprinkle 1 tablespoon of dry ingredients over the blueberries and set aside.

4. In a separate small bowl whisk the melted coconut, maple syrup, egg, and vanilla together until combined. Pour the wet ingredients into the dry ingredients, stir a few times, then add oat mixture and stir gently. Fold in blueberries.

5. Bake 20-25 minutes.

MAPLE PUMPKIN MUFFINS

INGREDIENTS:

1-3/4 cups gluten-free flour

¾ cup maple syrup

2 teaspoons baking powder

¼ teaspoon baking soda

½ teaspoon xanthan gum

½ teaspoon salt

1 teaspoon vanilla

2 teaspoons pumpkin pie spice

½ teaspoon cinnamon

3 large eggs

1 can (15-oz) pumpkin puree

½ cup coconut oil, melted

DIRECTIONS:

1. Preheat oven to 375 degrees. Grease 16 muffin cups.
2. In a large bowl, combine the dry ingredients.
3. In another bowl, beat together wet ingredients.
4. Add the wet ingredients to the bowl with the flour mixture. Stir just until combined—don't overmix.
5. Divide the mixture evenly between the prepared muffin cups.
6. Bake 26-30 minutes or until toothpick inserted into the center comes out clean.

GRAINLESS GARLIC BISCUITS

INGREDIENTS:

1 ½ cups almond flour

½ teaspoon salt

¼ teaspoon baking soda

1 tablespoon baking powder

½ teaspoon parsley

½ teaspoon onion powder

1 teaspoon garlic powder

1 cup goat cheese, shredded

2 eggs

½ cup unsweetened almond milk

2 tablespoons coconut oil, melted

DIRECTIONS:

1. Preheat oven to 450 degrees. Lightly spray paper liners in muffin pans.
2. In a small bowl add flour, salt, baking soda, baking powder, parsley, onion powder, garlic powder, and cheese and stir well.
3. Combine eggs, milk, and oil in a large bowl. Fold in flour mixture and mix until smooth.
4. Scoop into muffin pans.
5. Bake for 20-25 minutes.

GLUTEN FREE SANDWICH BREAD

INGREDIENTS:

1 TBSP YEAST

1 TBSP SUGAR

1 ½ CUP WARM WATER

2 ½ CUPS GLUTEN FREE
FLOUR MIX

1 TSP XANTHAN GUM

1 TBSP GROUND FLAXSEED

1 TSP SALT

3 EGGS

2 TBSP COCONUT OIL,
MELTED

1 TSP CIDER VINEGAR

DIRECTIONS:

1. Combine yeast and sugar

2. Add warm water to the yeast mixture and gently stir. Then allow this mixture to sit while you combine other ingredients.

3. In a separate bowl, combine flour, xanthan gum, flaxseed and salt—mix well.

4. In a third bowl, whisk eggs, oil, and vinegar until frothy.

5. Pour yeast and egg mixtures into the flour mixture and blend well

6. Line a loaf pan with parchment paper and spray generously with oil.

7. Scoop the dough into loaf pan.

8. Allow dough to rise in a warm area until it rises 1 in. from top of the of pan.

9. Bake at 375 degrees for 50-60 minutes.

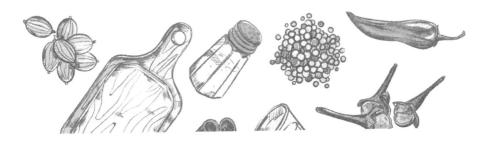

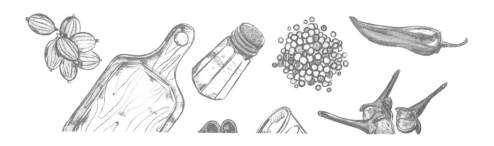

_____

_____

_____

_____

_____

_____

_____

_____

_____

_____

_____

_____

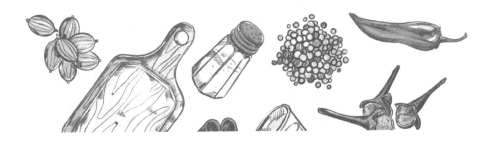

_____

_____

_____

_____

_____

_____

_____

_____

_____

_____

_____

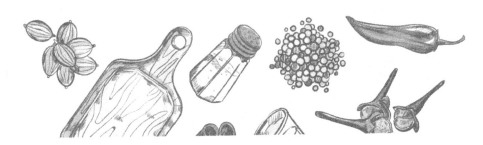

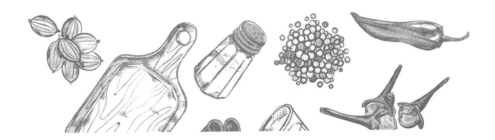

About the Author

Happiness lies, first of all, in health.
~George William Curtis

"For you have in your possession a
sacred trust. Guard it well."
~B. J. Palmer

"It's when we start working together that
the real healing takes place."
~David Hume

Dr. Lewis M. Clark graduated from Texas Chiropractic College in 1992, becoming a licensed Doctor of Chiropractic in the state of Texas that same year. Dr. Clark is a firm believer in ongoing education; therefore, his graduation from chiropractic college was only the beginning. He became a certified chiropractic wellness practitioner in 2008 through the International Chiropractic Association. He became board certified in integrative medicine in 2013 through the American Academy of Integrative Medicine.

In addition to these certifications, Dr. Clark is a graduate of the American Functional Neurology Institute and is currently enrolled in the Carrick Institute of Functional Neurology. Dr. Clark also continued his education in the realm of functional medicine, completing Dr.

Datis Kharrazian's functional blood chemistry analysis courses through Apex Energetics. This allows him to evaluate a person's blood work at a functional level and not just at a disease level.

He has also completed Dr. Kharrazian's Mastering the Thyroid and Mastering Blood-Brain Chemistry courses. Dr. Clark is certified in Trigenics Functional Muscle Neurology in upper extremities, a certified gluten practitioner, and a certified neuro cranial integration practitioner. He is also a certified Ziglar Legacy Trainer.

Currently, Dr. Clark attends functional neurology seminars and continues to study with other leaders in neurology and functional medicine through the NeuroMetabolic Super Group of Doctors.

Dr. Clark uses chiropractic and brain-based therapy, functional neurology, nutrition, and the latest technologies to help people recover from conditions such as fibromyalgia, chronic back pain, migraine headaches, autoimmune disorders like Hashimoto's disease, peripheral neuropathy, IBS (Irritable Bowel Syndrome), chronic knee pain, shoulder pain, ADD, and ADHD.

Because of the chronic conditions that Dr. Clark sees, he is also a certified gluten practitioner and specialist in food sensitivities, and the recovery of leaky gut, and autoimmunity conditions. He also helps people improve brain function to overcome insomnia, anxiety, depression, and brain fog through Brain-Based Therapy.

Dr. Clark is a firm believer in the body's ability to heal itself and often quotes, "The power that made the body, heals the body." Dr. Clark has assembled an amazing team to help him care for his patients. The combination of teamwork, technologies, and the right treatment options are what makes Clark Chiropractic & Wellness one of the premier wellness offices in the world. Dr. Clark is only able to accept a certain number of new patients and he promises to accept only those he feels certain he can help.

Personally, Dr. Lewis Clark is a Bible-believing Christian, and he and his wife, Rhonda, have 5 children and 8 grandchildren. They live with their family on a ranch in Cleveland, Texas called Middle Cross Ranch where they raise local, grass-fed beef for families interested in healthy meat options. He is an active member and teacher at East River Baptist Church.

The Clark Chiropractic Nutritional Coaching Solution

"Healing is an inside job."
~B. J. Palmer

Health is a relationship between you and your body."
~Terri Guillemets

"Labels are for cans, not people. We help people."
~Dr. Lewis Clark

Some of your most nagging problems can be directly related to what you're putting in your body. Fatigue, inflammation, trouble sleeping – all of these things are the result of poor nutrition and a lack of nutritional coaching.

The most important thing to remember when it comes to nutritional coaching and diet is that every person is different. The only way to truly tailor the ideal diet for yourself is by visiting a certified health coach.

At Clark Chiropractic and Wellness, we focus on total body solutions that deal with the root causes of your discomfort. Your diet is a major part of this process and plays a significant role in your quality of life.

If you have strayed from a healthy path, we're here to get you back on track.

Our nutritional team can help you get back to basics and set your body up for healthy living. That team is led by Rhonda Clark – a certified health coach with over 20 years of experience helping people rediscover their optimal state of living.

Don't chalk your symptoms up to simply "not feeling well" on any given day. If you find yourself frequently experiencing some or all these conditions, your next call should be to Rhonda Clark and the nutritional team at Clark Chiropractic and Wellness.

It's easy to simply take a look at the foods you might be eating and try to change around your diet by eliminating things, but this usually leads to short-term improvement at the cost of long-term results.

If you want to set yourself up with healthy habits and an effective lifestyle change that lasts, set up a consultation with Rhonda Clark and the nutrition team at Clark Chiropractic and Wellness.

The nutritional coaching at Clark Chiropractic and Wellness is fully individualized and customized based on your specific dietary needs. Dr. Lewis M. Clark and Rhonda Clark work together to help every client find out where the problems are in their lifestyle before making the necessary changes.

We believe in putting good things in before taking things away, helping you establish healthy changes, and achieve long-term health.

This process may begin with a functional blood analysis to see just what may be happening inside of your body – every person is different and each one requires a different level of care.

From here, we establish a nutritional and supplement plan to help you meet your goals and increase your overall quality of life. Rhonda Clark takes the guesswork out of the process with each of her client and helps them put their plan into action, including coaching on:

- how to buy foods
- how to prepare foods
- which foods to avoid
- the most effective lifestyle changes

Take control of your body and your diet by scheduling a consultation with Rhonda Clark and the nutritional team at Clark Chiropractic and Wellness today! Your body will be happy you did!

Address
562 Kingwood Dr.
Kingwood, TX 77339

Office Hours
Monday – Thursday
7:30 AM – 6:00 PM

Friday
7:30 AM – 12:00 PM

Start your pain-free journey today with a **free** (15-minute) consultation ($99 value). We can do these in person or virtually.

Call (281) 354-8330 to schedule your first appointment at Clark Chiropractic & Wellness. This is a limited time offer.

Connect with Clark Chiropractic:

Phone: (281) 354-8330
Website: http://www.clarkchiropractic.net
Facebook Page: http://www.facebook.com/clarkchiro92

Instagram: http://www.instagram.com/clarkchiro92
Pinterest: http://www.pinterest.com/clarkchiro92
Twitter: http://www.twitter.com/clarkchiro92

The Rest of the Story

*"What shall we then say to these things? If
God is for us, who can be against us?"*
~Romans 8:31 KJV

*"God will meet you where you are in order to
take you where He wants you to go."*
~Tony Evans

"There is no one who is insignificant in the purpose of God."
~Alistair Begg

Few would argue with the fact that we are three-part beings; physical, emotional, and spiritual. However, of these three little thought or effort is put into developing our spirit. There is even less acknowledgement that our spirit needs developing.

As a Bible believing Christian, there came a day when I heard, and believed the gospel of the Lord Jesus Christ, presented in the Bible. That day was in August 1996. On that day, I recognized myself as sinner. Not only had I been born into sin because of Adam's sin in the garden, but also, I had many times chosen to sin.

Therefore, I repented of my sin, acknowledged and agreed with God that I did not deserve His mercy, or eternal life and I put my faith and trust completely in the work of the Lord Jesus Christ on the cross to be the payment for my sin. The day that I put my faith and trust in Him, God began to give me peace, which I had not known before.

Since that time, I have continued to grow in my faith, develop my Spiritual health by talking to my Father in Heaven through prayer, and reading His words that He has written for me in the Bible, as well as attending my local church faithfully.

Studies show that an overwhelming percentage of Americans believe that there is a God. However, many have not thought about what this God is like, who He is, and what he requires of every one of us. There is obviously much confusion regarding how to have a right relationship with God.

However, reading the Bible, studying the Scriptures, and trusting in that alone will clear all the confusion. The Bible states that God, because He loves the world, sent His Son to be the payment for our sins that we could be saved from the penalty of sin, which is death.

It is my hope and prayer that you will be assured of having eternal life, which the Bible says in Romans 6:23 is only through Jesus Christ our Lord. If we can help you, or if you have any questions about how to have a relationship with God through Jesus Christ, contact us at our office.

The following verses are helpful if you are not familiar with your Bible:

*"For all have sinned, and come
short of the glory of God;"
~Romans 3:23 KJV*

*"But God commendeth his love toward us, in that,
while we were yet sinners, Christ died for us."
~Romans 5:8 KJV*

*"For the wages of sin is death; but the gift of God
is eternal life through Jesus Christ our Lord."
~Roman 6:23*

*"That if thou shalt confess with thy mouth the Lord Jesus,
and shalt believe in thine heart that God hath raised
him from the dead, thou shalt be saved.
For with the heart man believeth unto righteousness;
and with the mouth confession is made unto salvation."
~Romans 10:9-10*

Rhonda's Story

*"One cannot think well, love well, sleep
well, if one has not dined well."*
~Virginia Woolf

*"The best and most beautiful things in the world cannot be
seen or even touched. They must be felt with the heart."*
~Helen Keller

"God loves each of us as if there were only one of us."
~Saint Augustine

For Rhonda Clark, nutrition is more than a profession, it is her passion. For over twenty years, she has passionately studied and pursued the art of preparing healthy and delicious meals for her family.

Once her duties as a home school mom of three began to wind down, she enrolled and graduated from the Institute of Integrative Nutrition in 2018. Now she takes her passion, skill, and knowledge to the masses. Since that time, she has helped countless people to improve their health through nutrition and lifestyle changes.

Not only have people lost weight, decreased pain, and improved their mental capacity; they have also overcome many chronic illnesses through her leadership.

When she is not helping people recover their health with nutrition, she is taking care of her husband, Dr. Clark, and her three children at home as well as contributing to our ranch where we raise 100% grass fed beef.

She loves the outdoors, camping, and has even learned to love fishing thanks to her husband's persistence.

Appendix:
66 Names of
Added Sugars

Manufacturers add sugar to 74% of packaged foods sold in supermarkets.[21] The FDA requires food producers to list all ingredients in their foods. But added sugar comes in many forms and is often disguised using various unsuspecting names. That's why it's so hard to find added sugars on Nutrition Facts labels.

Here is a list of 66 names for added sugar in food products:

agave nectar/syrup	anhydrous dextrose
barley malt	Barbados sugar
beet sugar	brown rice syrup
brown sugar	buttered sugar or buttercream
cane juice	cane juice crystals
cane sugar	caramel

---

21 Ng, S.W., Slining, M.M., & Popkin, B.M. (2012). Use of caloric and non-caloric sweeteners in US consumer packaged foods, 2005–9. J Acad Nutr Diet. 2012 Nov; 112(11): 1828–1834.e6. https://www.ncbi.nlm.nih.gov/pmc/articles/PMC3490437/

carob syrup	castor sugar
coconut sugar	confectioner's (powdered) sugar
corn syrup	corn syrup solids
crystal dextrose	crystalline fructose
date sugar	demerara sugar
dextran	dextrin
dextrose	diastatic malt
diatase	ethyl maltol
evaporated cane juice	evaporated corn sweetener
Florida crystals	fructose
fruit juice	fruit juice concentrate
fruit nectar	galactose
glucose	glucose syrup solids
golden sugar	golden syrup
grape sugar	high-fructose corn syrup (HFCS)
honey	icing sugar
invert sugar	lactose
liquid fructose	malt syrup
maltodextrin	maltose
maple syrup	molasses
muscovado sugar	nectars (e.g., peach or pear nectar)
pancake syrup	panela sugar
panocha	raw sugar
sorghum syrup	sucanat
sucrose	sugar
sugarcane juice	turbinado sugar
white granulated sugar	yellow sugar

CPSIA information can be obtained
at www.ICGtesting.com
Printed in the USA
LVHW012154240821
696020LV00005B/13